MATHEMATICS WORKSHOP

MATH ON THE JOB

REVISED EDITION

Annotated Teacher's Edition

GLOBE FEARON EDUCATIONAL PUBLISHER
Upper Saddle River, New Jersey
www.globefearon.com

Copyright © 2000 updated materials:

Cover design: Marjory Dressler

Editorial management: Monica Glina

Development and production: Proof Positive/Farrowlyne Associates, Inc.

Printed in the United States of America

2 3 4 5 6 7 8 9 10 03 02 01

ISBN: 0-130-23361-7 (Student Edition)
ISBN: 0-130-23362-5 (Annotated Teacher's Edition)
Formerly titled *Exploring Careers*

GLOBE FEARON EDUCATIONAL PUBLISHER
Upper Saddle River, New Jersey
www.globefearon.com

TABLE OF CONTENTS

UNIT 1

Using Whole Numbers, Decimals, and Fractions

UNIT 1

Using Whole Numbers, Decimals, and Fractions

BANKER (PERSONAL BANKER)

Evelyn Holt works as a personal banker at a small bank in Cincinnati. She talks to customers every day about different ways to invest and save their money. A large portion of Evelyn's day is spent on the telephone soliciting local businesses to participate in one of several consumer credit card programs.

Walk-in customers often have questions or concerns about their credit card statements, and Evelyn must be able to help them. Explaining the interest rates, financial benefits, and payment schedules associated with each credit card program requires patience and a thorough knowledge of the way a credit card plan works.

EVALUATING CHARGES AND CREDITS

Many customers do not understand the charges and credits shown on their credit card statements, so Evelyn must help them understand how the charges and credits are determined. A *Transaction Summary* lists the charges made over a certain period of time. It also shows any payments or credits made to the customer's credit card account. An example of a *Transaction Summary* is shown below.

TRANSACTION SUMMARY

DATE		Credit	Charge
7 Jul	Everwear Department Store		$ 63.76
13 Jul	Family Pharmacy		$ 34.09
15 Jul	Payment	$150.00	
20 Jul	Lucky H Restaurant		$ 48.15
22 Jul	Payment	$ 75.00	
26 Jul	Lansing Liberty Daily News		$ 26.32
30 Jul	Big O Tires		$252.16

1. Based on the *Transaction Summary* shown above, what are the total credits for this credit card statement?

   $225.00

2. What are the total charges for this credit card statement?

   $424.48

UNDERSTANDING AN ACCOUNT SUMMARY

Credit card statements also show an *Account Summary*. A sample is shown below. The *Account Summary* lists the *Previous Balance; Transaction Total;* and *Payments, Credits, and Adjustments.* The *New Balance* on the summary will be calculated below.

Account Summary	
Previous Balance	$3,216.89
(−) Payments, Credits, and Adjustments	225.00
(+) Transactions	424.48
(+) Finance Charges	61.79
(=) New Balance	**$3,478.16**

The *New Balance* is calculated using the method below.

- Subtract *Payments, Credits, and Adjustments* from *Previous Balance.*
- Add *Transactions.*
- Add *Finance Charges.*

What is the *New Balance* for the *Account Summary* shown? Write your answer in the space provided above.

Using the same method, calculate the *New Balance* for each *Account Summary* shown below.

	Previous Balance		Payments, Credits, and Adjustments		Transactions		Finance Charges		New Balance
	$1,484.52	−	**$ 100**	+	**$ 74.78**	+	**$42**	=	**$1,501.30**
3.	$1,205.16		$ 100		$ 53.16		$37		$1,195.32
4.	$4,587.88		$ 500		$1,235.12		$87		$5,410.00
5.	$ 887.98		$ 600		$ 00		$32		$319.98
6.	$ 156.38		$ 25		$ 15.67		$15		$162.05
7.	$6,203.45		$2,500		$1,889.00		$98		$5,690.45
8.	$2,035.67		$ 950		$4,500.00		$76		$5,661.67
9.	$ 736.25		$ 00		$ 00		$28		$764.25
10.	$5,085.32		$1,200		$ 182.65		$92		$4,159.97

DETERMINING CREDIT LINES AND AVAILABLE CREDIT

Customers are frequently concerned about the amount of available credit they have on a credit card. Evelyn helps customers to see where, on their credit card statements, this information is listed. For example, a statement might indicate the *Total Available Credit* as shown below. As you can see in the example, *Total Available Credit* is determined by subtracting the *New Balance* from the *Total Credit Line.*

Total Credit Line	−	New Balance	=	Total Available Credit
$5,000	−	$4,159.97	=	$840.03

PERSONAL BANKER

Using the same method, calculate the values for *Total Available Credit* in the following examples.

	New Balance	Total Credit Line	Total Available Credit
11.	$1,195.32	$2,500	**$1,304.68**
12.	$ 5,410.00	$5,700	**$290.00**
13.	$ 319.98	$ 500	**$180.02**
14.	$ 162.05	$ 500	**$337.95**
15.	$5,690.45	$9,200	**$3,509.55**
16.	$5,661.67	$9,200	**$3,538.33**
17.	$ 764.25	$1,500	**$735.75**

COMPARING SAVINGS ACCOUNTS

Customers often have money they wish to invest. Choosing the best way to invest that money is one of Evelyn's many duties. She explains to a customer the different features of each savings account. Then she helps the customer make a sound financial decision. The table below describes the features of two different savings accounts.

	REGULAR SAVINGS	BONUS SAVINGS
Minimum Amount to Open	$100	$1,000
Monthly Service Fee	$9/quarter	$8/quarter
Monthly Service Fee Waived with	*Average Daily Balance* of $300 or more	*Average Daily Balance* of $1,000 or more

CALCULATING AN AVERAGE DAILY BALANCE

Many customers are concerned that they will be charged extra fees if their savings account balances fall below a required minimum. Usually, these fees are applicable only if the *Average Daily Balance* falls below a minimum. Like any other average, the *Average Daily Balance* is calculated by adding together the balance for each day of the month, then dividing by the total number of days in that month.

For example, here is how to calculate the *Average Daily Balance* for July.

(Balance on July 1) + . . . (Balance on July 31)/31 = *Average Daily Balance*

Use this method to help solve the following situation.

18. A customer has an established Bonus Savings Account with a balance of $5,000. On July 5, $4,500 had to be withdrawn to cover a family emergency. The $4,500 was replaced on July 27, but the customer is concerned that the account will be charged extra fees since it fell to $500 for a brief period.

To determine if the customer will be charged a fee, calculate the Average Daily Balance for this account during the month.

> **The account balance was at $5,000 from July 1–July 4 and from July 27–July 31, a total of**
>
> **9 days. The balance fell to $500 from July 5–July 26, a total of 22 days. The *Average Daily***
>
> ***Balance* for the account in July was therefore,**
>
> **[($5,000 x 9 days) + ($500 x 22 days)]/31 = [($45,000) + ($11,000)]/31 = $1,806.45**
>
> **The customer would be charged no fee since the balance was still above $1,000, the**
>
> **minimum *Average Daily Balance* required.**

If you were a Personal Banker, how would you handle the following situations?

19. A college student has $1,500 to deposit into a savings account. She would like the money to be available for purchasing some but not all of her textbooks and supplies. The student also plans on making additional small deposits throughout the school year. Which savings account would be the best choice for the student? Explain your answer.

> **Since the student plans on withdrawing small amounts from the account, it would**
>
> **probably make more sense to deposit the $1,500 into a Regular Savings Account. This way,**
>
> **if her *Average Daily Balance* falls below $1,000, there will be no fees charged to the account.**

20. A customer deposits an initial $2,300 into a Bonus Savings Account. During the remainder of the month, he makes three withdrawals of $425 each. What were his balances after each withdrawal? Will he be charged a fee for dropping below the minimum balance?

> **After the first withdrawal, the balance would have fallen to $1,875; after the second with-**
>
> **drawal—$1,450; after the third—$1,025. There will be no fees charged since the balance**
>
> **never fell below $1,000.**

---

*I*NSIDE *I*NFORMATION

A banker should:

- work patiently and effectively with customers
- have good communication skills
- be self-confident and able to handle rejections
- have good sales ability
- be able to work independently

Minimum Education: College graduate

Related Careers: Securities Sales
Representative, Insurance Agent

Starting Salary: $18,000–$24,300

SECRETARY

Karen Li is a secretary at a university. She works in the administrative office of the Mathematics and Computer Science Departments. The purpose of an administrative office is to make sure that an organization runs smoothly. In addition to word processing and taking telephone messages, some of Karen's duties are:

- processing student payroll forms
- processing travel requests and reimbursements
- operating a petty cash fund
- ordering office supplies

EVALUATING PAYROLL INFORMATION

One of Karen's jobs is to process payroll forms for students who work part-time as part of the College Work Study Program.

The computer science department has decided to hire Marie Song for a part-time position. Her financial aid information is given to the right.

Date: Feb. 3, 1999	
Marie Song Name	123-45-6789 Soc. Sec. No.
Computer Clerk Position	Computer Science Dept.
Walt Samuels Supervisor	
$5.15 Hourly Rate	$1,500 Work Study Limit

The student employees turn in their time sheets to Karen every Friday. She checks the following items:

- Has the student's supervisor signed the time sheets?
- Has the number of hours worked been correctly added up?
- Is the hourly rate for the student correct?
- Have the number of hours and the hourly rate been multiplied correctly?
- Has the student gone over his or her Work Study limit?

A timesheet for Marie Song is shown below. Complete the time sheet. Obtain information from her financial aid sheet when necessary. Write the number of hours in decimal form when necessary.

	NAME	Marie Song		SOC. SEC. NO.	123-45-6789
	POSITION	Computer Clerk		DEPARTMENT	Computer Science
	Month/Day/Year		Hours Worked		Number of Hours Worked
	02/06/99		1 P.M.–5 P.M.		4
1.	02/07/99		9 A.M.–1 P.M.		4
2.	02/08/99		2 P.M.–5:30 P.M.		3.5
3.	02/09/99		10 A.M.–2 P.M.		4
4.	02/10/99		9:30 A.M.–2:30 P.M.		5
5.	02/11/99		Didn't work		0
6.	02/12/99		11 A.M.–1 P.M.		2
7.	Total Number of Hours				22.5
8.	Hourly Rate		$5.15		
9.	Total Amount		$115.88		*Walt Samuels* Supervisor's Approval

10. Marie has earned a total of $455 so far this year. How much more money can she earn before she reaches her Work Study limit?

$1,045

11. How many more hours can Marie work before she reaches her Work Study limit?

203 hours

12. Albert Stephens worked 18.5 hours for the week ending on February 19. His salary is $5.30 per hour. He wrote $105.05 on his time sheet as his salary owed. How much should he actually be paid?

$98.05

13. As of the week ending on February 12, Albert's total earnings were $698.25. As of the week ending February 19, how much had Albert earned? Hint: you'll need to use your answer for Exercise 12.

$796.30

14. The total amount Albert is allowed to earn is $1,000. As of the week ending on February 19, how much more can he earn? Hint: you'll need to use your answer for Exercise 13.

$203.70

15. Shira Metzger has earned $853.00. The maximum amount she can earn is also $1,000. Her salary is $5.25 per hour. How many more hours can Shira work before she reaches her limit?

28 hours

MAINTAINING QUANTITIES OF OFFICE SUPPLIES

Karen orders supplies for every two weeks. Before she places her order, she makes a list of the supplies that are running low. She also asks whether there are any items that are needed in a hurry.

The supply room has a listing of the items they carry and the price of each item.

Here is a section of the listing:

Pads, stamp (black)	$2.19 ea.
Pads, stamp (red)	$2.19 ea.
Pads, white (8 1/2 x 11)	$0.75 ea.
Pads, yellow legal	$0.89 ea.
Paper, bond (white)	$2.50/ream
Pencil, #2	$1.49/box (10)
Pens, (black, fine pt.)	$2.98/box (10)
Pens, (blue, med pt.)	$2.75/box (10)
Rubber bands, (1/8 in.)	$3.15/box
Ruler, 12 in.	$0.85 ea.
Ruler, 15 in.	$0.95 ea.
Scissors	$5.30 ea.

Here is Karen's list:

2 Dozen Yellow Legal Pads
12 Reams White Bond Paper
9 Boxes of Pencils
3 Black Stamp Pads
3 Scissors
5 Boxes of Rubber Bands
3 Dozen White Pads (8½ x 11)

Use the information above to complete the Supply Requisition Form below.

SUPPLY REQUISITION FORM

	Item	Quantity	Unit Price	Total Price
	Pads, Yellow legal	24	$0.89	$ 21.36
16.	Paper, bond (white)	12	$2.50	$ 30.00
17.	Pencils, #2	9	$1.49	$ 13.41
18.	Pads, stamp (black)	3	$2.19	$ 6.57
19.	Scissors	3	$5.30	$ 15.90
20.	Rubber bands, (1/8 in.)	5	$3.15	$ 15.75
21.	Pads, white (8 1/2 x 11)	36	$0.75	$ 27.00
22.	Total Amount of Requisition			$129.99

8

SECRETARY

CALCULATING CASH FOR TRAVEL REQUESTS AND REIMBURSEMENTS

Professor Natalie Apted has been asked to make a speech at a mathematics conference in Denver, Colorado. She asks Karen to make the travel arrangements.

"I'd like to leave from Newark Airport on Friday, March 3, at around 3 P.M. I'll give my speech on Saturday, and be back on Sunday, March 5."

"Window or aisle?" Karen asks. "Also, are you going to need a rental car? And do you need a travel advance?"

"Window, please. I'll take a cab from the Denver airport. To cover the airfare, the hotel, my meals, and other expenses, I think I'll need $600 in cash."

Karen calls a travel agency to arrange for Professor Apted's flight. Then Karen gets $600 in cash from the university cashier for Professor Apted to use for her trip.

When Professor Apted returns from the conference, she fills out a travel reimbursement form.

Complete the form.

<table>
<tr><td colspan="6" align="center">**TRAVEL REIMBURSEMENT FORM**</td></tr>
<tr><td colspan="3">**NAME:** Natalie Apted</td><td colspan="3">**DATE FILED:** 3/31/99</td></tr>
<tr><td colspan="3">Purpose of Trip: Mathematics Conference in Denver, CO</td><td colspan="3">Dates of Travel: March 3–March 5</td></tr>
<tr><td>DATE</td><td>AIRFARE</td><td>HOTEL</td><td>MEALS</td><td>MISC.</td><td>TOTAL</td></tr>
<tr><td>**23.** 3/3/99</td><td>$275.00</td><td>85.00</td><td>28.93</td><td>45.00</td><td>$ 433.93</td></tr>
<tr><td>**24.** 3/4/99</td><td></td><td>85.00</td><td>56.43</td><td>6.75</td><td>$ 148.18</td></tr>
<tr><td>**25.** 3/5/99</td><td>$275.00</td><td></td><td>35.75</td><td>39.50</td><td>$ 350.25</td></tr>
<tr><td colspan="5">**26.** Subtotal</td><td>$ 932.36</td></tr>
<tr><td colspan="5">**27.** Travel advance</td><td>−($ 600.00)</td></tr>
<tr><td colspan="5">**28.** Total out-of-pocket expenses</td><td>$ 332.36</td></tr>
</table>

Karen is in charge of a petty cash fund of $250. *Petty cash* is a small amount of money that Karen has to pay for items under $50 that aren't available through the supply room or the bookstore. A person buys the item with his or her own money, brings the receipt to Karen, and is paid back.

If an item is $50 or more, Karen fills out a check request form for the person to sign. Once it has been approved by the Finance Officer, the employee receives the check in about 2 to 3 weeks.

29. Professor George Lee has just won the Best Professor Award. One of the assistants buys some bread, cheese, soda, and cookies for a party. The assistant brings in 4 different receipts: $9.58 for bread, $15.05 for cheese, $10.93 for soda, and $7.17 for cookies. How much money should Karen give the assistant?

   $42.73

30. A technician bought a can of tennis balls for $3.49, a set of children's wooden blocks for $8.03, and a dictionary for $31.84. The robotics lab needs these items to test the robotic arm they have built. Before the technician came in, Karen had $119.24 in her petty cash drawer. How much will be in the drawer after she reimburses the technician?

   $75.88

31. A scientist wants to be paid for a computer game he bought for $298.95. Karen tells the scientist she can't pay him back right away. Why?

   Sample answers: the limit for petty cash reimbursement is $50; there is at most $250 in

   the petty cash fund.

When the scientist finally left, Karen typed 5 letters for the Finance Officer and 3 letters for the Personnel Officer. By 4:30 P.M. all the letters had been signed. Karen made duplicate copies of the letters, filed the copies, and then mailed the letters.

It had been a normal workday—busy, full of a variety of tasks and problems, dealing with many people, keeping track of many things at once. Now it was time for Karen to go to her university night class in biology!

INSIDE INFORMATION

A secretary should:

- be able to type
- have good communication skills
- be familiar with office procedure

- be able to work under pressure
- have a knowledge of basic mathematics
- be organized and neat

Minimum Education: High-school graduate, basic office skills

Starting Salary: $17,400–$20,000 per year

Related Careers: Medical Secretary, Legal Secretary

RESTAURANT MANAGER

Bruce Canton is the night manager at a restaurant in Philadelphia. He works from 3:00 P.M. to 11:00 P.M. About 300 people are served at the restaurant each evening. The restaurant is cafeteria style, which means that there are no waiters or waitresses.

When Bruce arrives at the restaurant, he makes sure that his staff is on time. He also checks to make sure that there are enough food and supplies.

Then Bruce makes a log to record the money that is brought in and paid out. You will complete this log as you work through the lesson.

```
                        DAILY LOG

      Date: _____

      Beginning Cash          $236.00
                             _____

      Business              $2,347.16
                             _____

      Total Payout            $954.37
                             _____

      Supposed End Cash     $1,628.79
                             _____

      Actual End Cash       $1,651.04
                             _____

      Error                    $22.25
                             _____
```

MAINTAINING THE CASH REGISTER—BEGINNING CASH AND PAYOUTS

When Bruce arrived at work, there was $1,320.90 in the cash register. He left $236.00 in bills and coins in the cash register to "make a drawer." He put the rest of the money in the safe.

1. How much money did he put in the safe? __$1,084.90__

2. Write $236.00 in the **Beginning Cash** column of the daily log.

As customers paid for their meals during the evening, the amount of cash in the cash register continued to increase. Throughout the evening, deliveries were made to the restaurant. Bruce paid for deliveries using money from the cash register. He kept this list of payouts.

PAYOUTS   Date: _____

Bread	$ 41.75
Cheese	158.38
Sodas	316.12
Fish	123.05
Pasta	49.95
Supplies	150.15
Paper Goods	96.84
Potato Chips	**$18.13**

3. Just before 5:00 P.M., Bruce checked his list of expected deliveries and found that his order of potato chips had not arrived. Since most of the deliveries come between 9:00 A.M. and 5:00 P.M., he did not expect the delivery to arrive until the following day. He checked the supply of potato chips and found only a few bags left, not enough to last the evening. If you were Bruce, what would you do?

   <u>**Answers will vary. One possible solution is to buy more potato chips from a nearby**</u>

   <u>**supermarket.**</u>

4. Bruce solved the problem by giving one of the dishwashers a $20 bill from the cash register and sending him to the grocery store to buy potato chips. He told him to buy 7 large bags (enough to last the evening) and reminded him to get a receipt.

   When he returned, Bruce asked him for the receipt and the change. He gave Bruce $1.87 which he returned to the cash register. He then entered the cost of the potato chips to the list of payouts.

   How much did the potato chips cost? __**$18.13**__

5. Enter this amount to the list of payouts on page 11.

6. What was the total amount of payouts that Bruce made that evening? __**$954.37**__

7. Write this amount in the **Total Payout** column in the log of page 11.

ESTABLISHING GOOD CUSTOMER RELATIONS

Another important part of Bruce's job is to solve problems that arise with customers. Here are some of the typical problems that he encounters with customers.

8. A customer doesn't want to pay for her roast beef sandwich because she thinks the meat is too rare. What would you tell the customer?

   <u>**Answers will vary. One possible solution is to make a new sandwich for the customer.**</u>

9. Some teenagers are playing a radio at their table. Several customers complain that the music is too loud. What would you do?

   <u>**Answers will vary. One possible answer is to ask the students to turn down the radio.**</u>

10. A customer complains that the cashier has given him the wrong change. The customer says he gave the cashier a $20 bill, but the cashier is sure that it was a $10 bill. What would you do?

    <u>**Answers will vary. One possible answer is to assume that the customer is telling the truth**</u>

    <u>**and give him change from $20.**</u>

RESTAURANT MANAGER

EVALUATING EMPLOYEE TIME RECORDS AND WAGES

Bruce kept a record of the number of hours each employee worked during the evening. Each night he attaches this record to his cash report. Complete the following time record.

EMPLOYEE TIME RECORD				
Employee	Job	Hourly Rate	Hours Worked	Wages
11. Jan	Cook	$ 12.00	8	$ 96.00
12. Al	Counter	5.15	7	36.05
13. Maria	Counter	5.15	6.5	33.48
14. James	Counter	5.15	7	36.05
15. Ellen	Counter	5.15	7.5	38.63
16. Karen	Counter	5.15	7	36.05
17. Bob	Dishwasher	5.50	8	44.00
18. Jo	Baker	9.00	6	54.00
19. Paul	Cleanup	7.50	5	37.50
20. Steve	Cashier	6.00	8	48.00
21. Bruce	Manager	16.00	8	128.00
22. TOTAL AMOUNT PAID IN WAGES				$587.76

When the restaurant closed, Bruce "closed out the register." This means he pushed the code buttons so that the amount of business for the evening was printed out on a receipt. The receipt, which showed every sale, totaled $2,347.16.

23. Write $2,347.16 in the **Business** column of the daily log on page 11.

    Bruce needed to find the amount of money that should be in the cash register. He used the following formula to find the **Supposed End Cash.**

    Beginning Cash   +   Business   −   Total Payout   =   Supposed End Cash

24. Use this formula to calculate the **Supposed End Cash.** Use the data from the daily log on page 11.

$ 236.00	+	$ 2,347.16	−	$ 954.37	=	$ 1,628.79
Beginning Cash		*Business*		*Total Payout*		*Supposed End Cash*

25. What is the amount that should be in the cash register? __$ 1,628.79__

26. Write this amount in the **Supposed End Cash** column of the daily log on page 11.

Next, Bruce counted the money in the cash register to find the amount of money in the register, the **Actual End Cash.** If the amount differs from the **Supposed End Cash**, then there was an error of some kind.

Bruce used this list to help him count the money. Find the total amount for each category.

	Bills	Number of Bills	Total		Coins	Number of Coins	Total
27.	$100	1	$100	**33.**	Quarters	26	$6.50
28.	$50	2	$100	**34.**	Dimes	37	$3.70
29.	$20	37	$740	**35.**	Nickels	28	$1.40
30.	$10	45	$450	**36.**	Pennies	44	$0.44
31.	$5	38	$190	**37.**	TOTAL AMOUNT OF CASH		$1,651.04
32.	$1	59	$59				

38. Enter this amount in the **Actual End Cash** column of the daily log on page 11.

Bruce compared the **Actual End Cash** to the **Supposed End Cash** to see if the amounts matched.

39. Are the amounts the same? _____ no _____

40. Which amount is greater? actual end cash

41. Find the difference between **Actual End Cash** and **Supposed End Cash.** _____ $22.25 _____

42. Enter this amount in the **Error** column of the daily log on page 11.

43. How would you explain this error to the owner of the restaurant? What might be some of the causes of this error?

Answers will vary. Possible answers include giving an incorrect amount of change or

counting cash in the register incorrectly.

Do you think that the job of a restaurant manager might be for you? If so, read on.

INSIDE INFORMATION

A restaurant manager should:

- be organized
- be able to solve problems quickly
- know about food preparations and storage

- like to work with a variety of people
- have a solid understanding of how to compute with whole numbers, fractions, decimals, and amounts of money

Minimum Education: Associate's degree, bachelor's degree, or certification in restaurant and food service management

Related Careers: Hotel Management

Starting Salary: $16,640–$25,061 per year

CASHIER

Larry Isaacs has been a cashier at an airport duty-free shop for almost five years. Larry is responsible for totaling bills, receiving money, making change, filling out charge forms, and giving receipts. He also handles currency exchange from various countries. The duty-free shop sells all kinds of gifts and personal items. The shop is called "duty free" because it doesn't charge taxes (duty) on the items. Since it is located at the airport, the shop accepts money from many different foreign countries.

COUNTING OUT CHANGE TO A CUSTOMER

When a customer pays using cash, there is usually change owed the customer. This is the difference between the total owed and the amount of money the customer gives the cashier. When Larry gives a customer change, he counts out the change starting with the *Purchase Total* and ends with the amount the customer gave him. This shows the customer exactly how much change the customer is receiving and also helps eliminate errors. An example is shown below.

Example: Suppose a customer bought items totaling $23.65. Larry receives $30.00 from the customer and, therefore, owes the customer $6.35 in change. Here is how the change is returned to the customer.

Start with the *Purchase Total* ($23.65) then begin counting toward the amount the customer paid ($30.00).

Begin counting out change using the coins.

Purchase Total +	(10¢) +	(25¢)
$23.65	$23.75	$24.00

Now continue counting out the customer's change with the bills until the amount paid by the customer, $30 in this case, is reached.

$24.00 +	($1) +	($5)
	$25.00	$30.00

In the table below, start with the *Purchase Total*, then refer to the number of coins and bills shown to count out the change. You should stop counting when you reach the **Amount Paid.**

	Purchase Total										Amount Paid
	$10.20	5¢	25¢	25¢	25¢	$1	$1	$1	$1	$5	$20.00
		$10.25,	$10.50,	$10.75,	$11,	$12,	$13,	$14,	$15,	$20	
1.	$7.45	5¢	25¢	25¢	$1	$1					$10.00
		$7.50,	$7.75,	$8,	$9,	$10,					
2.	$3.80	10¢	10¢	$1							$5.00
		$3.90,	$4.00,	$5,							
3.	$14.95	5¢	$5								$20.00
		$15.00,	$20,								
4.	$37.15	10¢	25¢	25¢	25¢	$1	$1				$40.00
		$37.25,	$37.50,	$37.75,	$38.00,	$39,	$40,				
5.	$26.80	10¢	10¢	$1	$1	$1	$5	$5			$40.00
		$26.90,	$27.00,	$28,	$29,	$30,	$35,	$40,			

MAINTAINING THE CASH DRAWER

At the beginning of his shift, Larry is given a "bank" of money for his register drawer. During the shift, Larry takes *Cash In* from customer sales and pays *Cash Out* when he gives change. At the end of the shift, Larry must make sure the amount of cash in his register drawer equals the amount of the *"Bank"* plus the *Cash In* from sales, minus the *Cash Out.*

Calculate the amount that should be in the register drawer at the end of a cashier's shift.

	"Bank"		Cash In		Cash Out		Cash
	(Beginning of shift) e.g., $250	+ +	**(from Sales)** **$567**	– –	**(from Change)** **$47.50**	= =	**(End of shift)** **$769.50**
6.	$250		$897.36		$119.42		$ 1,027.94
7.	$250		$417.85		$83.29		$ 584.56
8.	$250		$359.12		$72.06		$ 537.06
9.	$500		$1,280.54		$86.88		$ 1,693.66
10.	$500		$2,451.29		$128.49		$ 2,822.80

CASHIER

COUNTING CASH USING MULTIPLES

When handling large amounts of cash, it is easier to count using multiples. For example, the total number of a stack of $10 bills can be multiplied by ten, $5 bills can be multiplied by five, quarters can be multiplied by $.25, and so on. Calculate the **Cash Totals** below by using the multiples given for each type of coin or bill.

	25¢	$1	$5	$10	$20	Cash Total
Multiple:	64	15	8	8	5	$251.00
11.	32	8	6	5	8	$256.00
12.	29	5	5	7	4	$187.25
13.	25	15	7	10	5	$256.25
14.	42	15	8	9	4	$235.50
15.	30	11	9	12	6	$303.50
16.	64	16	3	16	8	$367.00

EXCHANGING FOREIGN CURRENCY

Below is part of the conversion chart that Larry uses to figure out prices and to make change in different currencies. The first line of Larry's chart gives the conversion rate, or the equivalent of $1.00 (U.S.) in foreign currencies. This enables Larry to compute prices that are not shown on a regular price list. For example, suppose you want to find the number of yen in $5.00. The chart shows that $1.00 is equivalent to 115.42 yen. To find the equivalent of $5.00 in yen, you multiply: $5.00 x 115.42 = 577.10.

Use the conversion rate and a calculator to find each price in the conversion chart.

COUNTRY CURRENCY	U.S. Dollar	Germany Mark	Canada Dollar	Italy Lira	Japan Yen
Actual Conversion Rate $1.00 U.S.	$1.00	1.67	1.55	1,654.00	115.42
GIFTS					
17. Belt	38	63.46	58.90	62,852.00	4,385.96
18. Scarf	43	71.81	66.65	71,122.00	4,963.06
19. Sunglasses	105	175.35	162.75	173,670.00	12,119.10
20. Necklace	80	133.60	124.00	132,320.00	9,233.60
21. Calculator	23	38.41	35.65	38,042.00	2,654.66

*I*NSIDE *I*NFORMATION

A cashier should:

- be able to work with numbers
- have a fairly high degree of eye-hand coordination
- be able to work well with the public
- be able to do repetitious work accurately

Minimum Education: High-school graduate
        with some work experience is
        desirable but not always required.

Starting Salary: $165–$247 per week

Related Careers: Bank Tellers, Postal Service Clerks

CHEF

Carl Glazier works as a chef at a small, downtown bistro in Chicago. His busy day includes the preparation, seasoning, and cooking of salads, soups, fish, meats, vegetables, and desserts. The menu is planned and priced, supplies are ordered, and the cooks are supervised.

During peak hours, Carl pays close attention to food preparation times and any dwindling supplies of key ingredients. He personally checks to see that all meals are presented and garnished properly, with no details overlooked. At the end of each week, Carl evaluates the menu to make any necessary changes.

MULTIPLYING QUANTITIES IN RECIPES

Many recipes are initially written for only a small number of servings. At the bistro when a new recipe is incorporated into the menu, Carl must increase the number of servings that the original recipe yielded in order to accommodate a large number of customers. Below is a list of the ingredients needed for a frequently requested dessert, Chocolate Bread Pudding with Custard Sauce, that Carl had to increase several times for use in the bistro.

Multiply the quantities of ingredients listed below by the correct factor to get the number of servings shown.

Chocolate Bread Pudding
(12 servings)

Ingredients	36 servings	48 servings
Example: 6 large eggs	× 3 = 18 eggs	× 4 = 24 eggs
1. $1\frac{1}{4}$ cups sugar	$3\frac{3}{4}$ cups	5 cups
2. $\frac{2}{3}$ tablespoon vanilla	2 Tb.	$2\frac{2}{3}$ Tb.
3. $\frac{3}{4}$ tablespoon instant espresso powder	$2\frac{1}{4}$ Tb.	3 Tb.
4. $2\frac{1}{3}$ cups whipping cream	7 cups	$9\frac{1}{3}$ cups
5. $\frac{1}{2}$ stick unsalted butter	$1\frac{1}{2}$ sticks	2 sticks
6. 12 ounces bittersweet or semisweet chocolate	36 oz.	48 oz.
7. 1 loaf cinnamon bread	3 loaves	4 loaves

8. $2\frac{3}{4}$ cups whole milk $8\frac{1}{4}$ cups _____   11 cups _____

9. 10 egg yolks   30 yolks _____   40 yolks _____

10. $\frac{4}{5}$ cup sugar $2\frac{2}{5}$ cups _____ $3\frac{1}{5}$ cups _____

11. $2\frac{3}{8}$ teaspoons vanilla $7\frac{1}{8}$ tsp. _____ $9\frac{1}{2}$ tsp. _____

COMBINING QUANTITIES

Dry goods are used extensively in the preparation of breads; to thicken soups, chowders, gravies, and sauces; for pastry crusts; and for baking. At the end of the week, when supplies of dry goods begin to run low, Carl orders more. To determine how much to order, he first combines the amounts required for each menu item for one week.

Amounts Required for One Week

		Entrees		Breads		Soups		Desserts		Weekly Total
12.	Flour	$5\frac{2}{3}$ lb	+	$56\frac{1}{3}$ lb	+	$\frac{2}{3}$ lb	+	$3\frac{1}{3}$ lb	=	66 lb
13.	White Sugar	$\frac{3}{4}$ lb	+	$4\frac{1}{4}$ lb	+	$\frac{1}{2}$ lb	+	$2\frac{3}{4}$ lb	=	$8\frac{1}{4}$ lb
14.	Brown Sugar	$\frac{1}{3}$ lb	+	$2\frac{1}{2}$ lb	+	none	+	$28\frac{2}{3}$ lb	=	$31\frac{1}{2}$ lb
15.	Salt	$\frac{4}{5}$ lb	+	$\frac{1}{3}$ lb	+	$\frac{2}{3}$ lb	+	$\frac{1}{5}$ lb	=	2 lb

Next, Carl subtracts the amounts that are on hand from the weekly amounts. Use the answers above to fill in the blanks below for each *Weekly Amount*. Then subtract the amounts *On Hand* to determine the *Amount to Order* of each item.

		Weekly Amount		*On Hand*		*Amount to Order*
16.	Flour	66 lb	–	$8\frac{2}{3}$ lb	=	$57\frac{1}{3}$ lb
17.	White Sugar	$8\frac{1}{4}$ lb	–	$4\frac{1}{2}$ lb	=	$3\frac{3}{4}$ lb
18.	Brown Sugar	$31\frac{1}{2}$ lb	–	$4\frac{1}{4}$ lb	=	$27\frac{1}{4}$ lb
19.	Salt	2 lb	–	$\frac{1}{3}$ lb	=	$1\frac{2}{3}$ lb

CHEF

CONVERTING CUPS TO POUNDS

Most recipes use the same unit of measurement, a cup, for dry ingredients like flour and sugar. Carl totals the number of cups of flour or sugar needed for a week to determine how many pounds of flour or sugar to order. There are about 18 cups of flour in a 5 pound bag; about 10 cups of white sugar in a 5 pound bag; and about 11 cups of brown sugar in a 5 pound bag. In the following exercises, see if you can convert cups to pounds and determine the number of 5 pound bags needed.

20. If a total of 66 lb of flour, $36\frac{1}{2}$ lb of white sugar, and $27\frac{1}{4}$ lb of brown sugar are needed for the week, about how many 5 pound bags of each of these ingredients should be ordered? Be sure to round up so that supplies do not run out.

_____fourteen 5 lb bags of flour; eight 5 lb bags of white sugar; six 5 lb bags of brown sugar_____

_____

_____

21. About how many cups of flour will be obtained from 66 lb? How many cups of white sugar from $36\frac{1}{2}$ lb? How many cups of brown sugar from $27\frac{1}{4}$ lb? Round answers up to the next whole number.

_____66 lb flour = 238 cups; $36\frac{1}{2}$ lb white sugar = 73 cups; $27\frac{1}{4}$ lb brown sugar = 160 cups_____

_____

_____

22. By the middle of the week, Carl notices that there are six 5 lb bags of flour and four 5 lb bags of white sugar left to last through the week. Referring to weekly amounts used previously, what should Carl do?

_____Since 66 lb of flour are needed for the week, the six 5 lb bags will not be sufficient. Two_____

_____or three more bags should be purchased to get through the week and a note made to change_____

_____the weekly amount. Since $36\frac{1}{2}$ lb of sugar are needed for the week and there are four 5 lb_____

_____bags left, this leaves twenty pounds for the remainder of the week. There is no need to order_____

_____more sugar._____

_____

_____

Before Carl submits a purchase order for supplies, he double-checks the amounts and prices. Below is a copy of the purchase order Carl submitted for the coming week. Calculate the totals for each of the three items and for the **Total Amount Due.**

From: Le Bon Bistro
100 River Street
Chicago, Illinois

To: Wholesale Dry Goods
231 East 10th Avenue
Chicago, Illinois

Quantity	Item	Price per 5 lb.	Amount
23. 15	Flour	$2.76	$41.40
24. 8	White Sugar	$3.42	$27.36
25. 6	Brown Sugar	$3.70	$22.20
26. Total Amount Due			$90.96

27. Carl normally rounds up quantities of ingredients. Why is this a good idea? What kinds of unexpected events might occur that would require more than the estimated amount of ingredients?

   Some meals might have to be recooked due to customer complaints. Other dishes

   might be ruined due to overcooking or other human error. Extra supplies will help cover

   these unexpected but inevitable situations.

INSIDE INFORMATION

A chef should:

- be original and creative
- be able to schedule work and activities
- have good manual dexterity
- be able to supervise and lead others

Minimum Education: Applicable work experience or certification from a culinary arts school

Starting Salary: $6.00–$8.00 per hour

Related Careers: Head Baker, Head Cook

INSURANCE AGENT

Adele Swanson is an agent for an insurance company in Michigan. Her company sells health, life, disability, automobile, and homeowner's insurance.

Adele spends about two days a week traveling to the homes and businesses of her customers. On a typical day, Adele may visit five to twelve customers.

Certain terms must be understood when writing or reading an insurance policy.

Insured – the person or persons covered by an insurance policy.

Premium – the rate paid for insurance each year.

Deductible – the amount of money that is subtracted or "deducted" from an insurance payment. For example, suppose a customer submits a claim for $450.00 to replace a damaged front grill on a car. If the customer's policy has a deductible of $100.00, the insurance company will pay the customer $350.00 ($450.00 minus the $100.00 deductible).

Short Term Coverage – temporary health insurance (30–185 days) for people who are between permanent health plans.

Adele has recently met the Twyford family. They are moving to the area and would like to purchase short-term medical insurance for three months until Mr. and Mrs. Twyford have begun their new jobs. To determine how much insurance the Twyford family needs for the three month period and what that insurance will cost, Adele first uses a ZIP Code Factor Table.

ZIP Code Factor Table
Find the first three digits of you resident address ZIP code in the ZIP Code column. Locate the multiplication factor in the Factor column. If your specific ZIP code is not shown, use the factor for All Others.

ZIP Code	Factor
485	.65
480, 481, 483	.75
482	.95
All Others in Michigan	.55

COMPUTING INSURANCE PREMIUMS

To compute the annual **premium,** Adele must know the ZIP code factor of the person who wants to buy insurance. The person's ZIP code factor is determined by the first three digits of the ZIP code. Use the ZIP Code Factor Table on page 23 to answer the following questions.

Find the correct ZIP Code Factor.

	City in Michigan	First 3 Digits of ZIP Code	Factor
1.	Detroit	482	.95
2.	Sylvan Lake	483	.75
3.	Flint	485	.65
4.	Birmingham	480	.75
5.	Hillman	497	.55

6. The Twyfords are looking at homes in Detroit, Flint, or further north in Hillman. Where should they live in order to have the lowest ZIP code factor?

   Hillman, where the ZIP Code Factor is .55

Here is the Monthly Payment table.

MONTHLY PREMIUMS				
Nonrenewable Short Term Medical Coverage (12/98) $500 and $1,000 Deductible/$2 million coverage maximum per policy period				
	$500 Ded.		$1,000 Ded.	
Age	M	F	M	F
0–24	$ 1.92	$2.16	$1.44	$1.56
25–29	1.92	2.28	1.44	1.68
30–34	2.16	2.88	1.44	2.04
35–39	2.64	3.36	1.80	2.40
40–44	3.24	3.72	2.28	2.76
45–49	3.72	4.32	3.00	3.36
50–54	5.04	5.04	3.96	3.72
55–59	7.08	6.36	5.28	4.80
60–64	9.96	7.32	7.56	5.52
1 Child	$1.20		$0.96	
2 Children	2.28		1.80	
3+ Children	3.24		2.64	
M=Male F=Female Rates shown are daily. These Monthly Payments are based on a minimum policy period of 35 days.				

Exercises 7–14 are regarding monthly premiums for Short Term Medical Coverage as shown in the table above.

7. Mr. Twyford is 31 years old. Mrs. Twyford is 29 years old. The Twyfords have one child, age 6. If the Twyfords live in Detroit, what will their $500 deductible premium be for 35 days?

   $187.53

INSURANCE AGENT

8. What would the 60 day premium be with a
$1,000 deductible for a single woman, age 37, living in Flint? _____ **$93.60** _____

9. In which city will the premiums be higher, Birmingham or Sylvan Lake?

The ZIP Code Factor is the same; therefore the premiums would be the same.

10. Steve Johnson is 27 years old and lives in Hillman.
What would his $500 deductible premium be for a 45 day policy period? _____ **$47.52** _____

11. Susan Davis is 24 years old. She is engaged to
Steve Johnson. As husband and wife, what will
their $1,000 deductible premium be for 60 days, assuming they live in Hillman? _____ **$99.00** _____

12. Check the 35 day, $500 deductible premiums for females age 55 for both Detroit
and Flint. Compare them with the 35 day, $500 deductible premiums for
males age 55. Are the premiums higher or lower for females age 55? _____ **Lower** _____

13. At what ages are the premiums the same for men and women?

For $500 deductible at age 50–54

14. Why do you think the premiums for women are more than those for men before the age of 54 but
less than the premiums for men after age 54?

Answers may vary. Possible answers include: Those women spend more on health care

than those men. For example, they have babies.

15. Once they are settled in their new home, the Twyford family decides to purchase a long-term
renewable $250,000 Major Medical policy with $1,000 deductible. Most long-term renewable plans
offer discounts to nonsmokers. Neither Mr. nor Mrs. Twyford has ever smoked. Find their non-
smoker discount in the table below.

$17.00

AMOUNT OF ANNUAL NONSMOKER DISCOUNT
(All ZIP Codes)

Age of Person Insured	Type of Plan	$250	$500	$1,000	$2,000	Age of Person Insured	Type of Plan	$250	$500	$1,000	$2,000	Age of Person Insured	Type of Plan	$250	$500	$1,000	$2,000
			Deductible						Deductible						Deductible		
21–24	Male	$10	$ 8	$ 5	$ 4	35–39	Male	$17	$14	$ 9	$ 8	50–54	Male	$51	$40	$25	$21
	Female	16	10	8	7		Female	28	18	16	13		Female	62	41	36	31
	Family	26	17	11	10		Family	45	29	22	19		Family	110	75	55	47
25–29	Male	11	9	6	5	40–44	Male	22	18	11	9	55–59	Male	74	56	39	33
	Female	21	13	10	9		Female	36	23	21	18		Female	74	56	39	33
	Family	31	20	15	12		Family	57	38	29	24		Family	143	103	71	60
30–34	Male	13	10	7	6	45–49	Male	26	20	13	11	60–64*	Male	93	71	50	43
	Female	24	15	13	11		Female	43	27	25	21		Female	93	71	50	43
	Family	36	23	17	15		Family	67	44	34	29		Family	180	131	90	77
												*Renewal Only					

COMPLETING A PREMIUM COMPUTATION FORM

Now you are able to complete the Short Term Premium Computation Form below. Refer to the information you have obtained from answering earlier questions.

Check the appropriate boxes and fill in all of the lines.

SHORT TERM PREMIUM COMPUTATION FORM

16. Name of Insured __Twyford Family_____

17. ZIP Code Factor

18. Deductible: [   ] $500   [✓] $1,000

19. Basic Daily rate $ __Answers will vary.__

20. Policy period   × $ __Answers will vary.__

21. Subtotal $ __Answers will vary.__

22. ZIP Code Factor   × $ __Answers will vary.__

23. Short Term Premium without Policy Fee $ __Answers will vary.__

24. Policy Fee   + $ __Answers will vary.__

25. TOTAL SHORT TERM PREMIUM $ __Answers will vary.__

---

*I*NSIDE *I*NFORMATION

An insurance agent should:

- like to sell
- be outgoing and comfortable meeting all types of people
- be able to handle rejection when customers decide not to buy insurance
- be organized and able to plan a work schedule
- be able to work alone
- be familiar with computers and software packages

Minimum Education: College Graduate,
    Business School helpful
    All states require insurance
    agents to be licensed.

Related Careers: Real Estate Agent,
    Insurance Broker

Starting Salary: $21,100–$49,000 per year
    Note: May be paid by salary only,
    salary plus commission, or salary plus
    bonus.

REGISTERED NURSE

Juanita Flores is a registered nurse (R.N.) in a large hospital. She helps treat people whose kidneys do not work properly by giving them **dialysis** treatments. Doctors and nurses use dialysis machines to help perform the functions that the patients' kidneys are unable to perform properly.

Juanita has three main responsibilities: keeping a watch of patients' health, giving treatments using the dialysis machines, and alerting doctors to any unusual situations.

COLLECTING PATIENT DATA

A patient on dialysis comes to the hospital three or four times a week for treatment. At each visit, an R.N. checks the patient's weight, dry weight, blood pressure, and pulse. In this way, the R.N. becomes familiar with the patient's normal readings for these statistics. Readings that are far from a patient's normal readings let the R.N. know that there may be a change in the patient's condition that the doctor should know about immediately.

Below are explanations of key statistics.

Weight – When dialysis patients come to the hospital, they usually have weights greater than their normal weights. This is because the patients' kidney problems cause their bodies to retain, or keep in, extra fluids.

Dry Weight – This is the normal weight that the patient would have if fluid was not being retained. Dialysis treatments get rid of this extra fluid and bring the patient back down to his or her dry weight, or target weight.

Pulse – This is the number of times a heart beats per minute. For adults, a pulse within the range of 60 to 90 beats per minute is normal. Pulse and blood pressure must be checked to make sure that it is safe to put a patient on the dialysis machine.

Blood Pressure – This is the pressure of blood against the inner walls of the blood vessels inside your body. Blood pressure is written with two numbers such as 140/80. The first number gives the highest pressure, which occurs when the heart is beating. The second number gives the lowest pressure, which occurs between heartbeats.

Temperature – This is the patient's body temperature.

Use the explanations above to answer the questions.

1. Why do dialysis patients gain weight between treatments? The patients' kidney problems cause their bodies to retain fluids.

2. Suppose a dialysis patient comes in for a treatment. Would you expect his or her weight before the treatment to be greater or less than his or her dry weight? Explain. _____

    __The patient's weight would be greater before the treatment because dialysis eliminates__

    __the extra fluid in the body.__

3. What does it mean to say that a person has a pulse of 90? _____

    __The person's heart is beating 90 times in one minute.__

4. Why is it important for a R.N. to see the same patients every week for dialysis? _____

    __The R.N. becomes familiar with the patients' normal readings and can alert the doctor__

    __when there are changes in the patients' conditions.__

5. Why must the R.N. check a patient's pulse and blood pressure before each treatment? _____

    __To make sure that it is safe to put the patient on the dialysis machine.__

DETERMINING ACCURATE SETTINGS FOR DIALYSIS MACHINES

When the R.N. is sure that it is safe to go ahead with the treatment, he or she uses three factors to set the dialysis machine:

- the patient's weight
- the patient's dry weight and target weight
- treatment time, as determined by the doctor

The treatment time is the length of time that the patient is on the dialysis machine. Treatments usually last from 3.5 to 5 hours.

To set the dialysis machine for a person with a weight of 196 lbs, a target weight of 182 lbs, and a treatment time of 5 hours, the R.N. would make the following calculations:

- Find the desired weight loss.

        → Weight − target weight = weight loss desired
            196 − 182 = 14 lbs

- Convert weight loss to kilograms (1 kg ≈ 2 lb)*.

        →   14 ÷ 2 = 7 kg

- Convert weight loss in kg to fluid loss in liters (1 kg ≈ 1 L).

        →   7 kg ≈ 7 L

- Divide to find the hourly rate of fluid loss. →   7 L ÷ 5 hr = 1.4 L an hour

* Note: ≈ means *approximately equal to*. 1 kg ≈ 2.2 lb. However, the conversion [1 kg ≈ 2 lb] is often used for this computation because division is easier with 2 pounds, and the results are close enough.

Name _____ Class _____ Date _____

REGISTERED NURSE

Complete the chart. Use 1 kg ≈ 2 lb.

	Weight (in lbs)	Target Weight	Treatment Time (in hrs)	Desired Weight Loss (in lbs)	Desired Weight Loss (in kg)	Desired Fluid Loss (in L)	Hourly Rate of Fluid Loss (in L)
6.	146	140	4	6	3	3	0.75
7.	188	178	5	10	5	5	1
8.	126	118	5	8	4	4	0.8
9.	262	244	4.5	18	9	9	2
10.	157	150	3.5	7	3.5	3.5	1
11.	132	127	4	5	2.5	2.5	0.625

EVALUATING PATIENT DATA

Originally, the doctor determines the treatment that the dialysis patient must receive. However, after the patient begins treatment, the doctor relies on the R.N.'s experience and judgment to carry out the doctor's orders.

Since the registered nurse sees the patient regularly, he or she is familiar with the patient's regular heart and weight data. If that data is outside the patient's normal ranges either before or after the treatment, it is the R.N.'s responsibility to alert the doctor. Below is an example of this type of case. On the left is part of a chart that the R.N. uses. The patient's normal ranges are on the right.

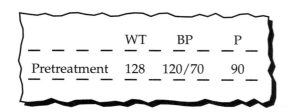

Normal Ranges

Dry Weight: 114
Weight: 114–122
BP: 120/70–130/80
Pulse: 80–90

Key: WT = Weight in Pounds, BP = Blood Pressure, P = Pulse

In this case, the patient's pretreatment readings caused the R.N. to alert the doctor. Because the patient had gained so much weight, the doctor decided that it was not safe to bring the patient all the way down to the normal dry weight during the treatment.

Look at the information below. Then identify the data that might cause the R.N. to alert the doctor.

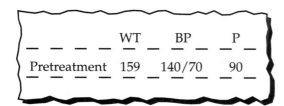

Normal Ranges

Dry Weight: 150
Weight: 150–161
BP: 120/60–130/70
Pulse: 70–80

12. Is any of the data unusual? Explain. __**Pretreatment blood pressure and pulse rate are**__

__**higher than normal.**__

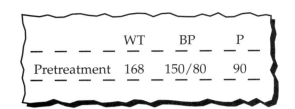

Normal Ranges

Dry Weight: 156
Weight: 156–162
BP: 150/80–140/70
Pulse: 80–90

	WT	BP	P
Pretreatment	168	150/80	90

13. Is any of the data unusual? Explain. **Pretreatment weight is higher than normal.**

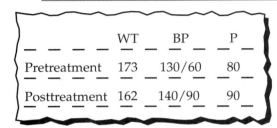

Normal Ranges

Dry Weight: 162
Weight: 162–174
BP: 120/60–130/70
Pulse: 70–80

	WT	BP	P
Pretreatment	173	130/60	80
Posttreatment	162	140/90	90

14. Is any of the data unusual? Explain. **Posttreatment blood pressure and pulse rate are higher than normal.**

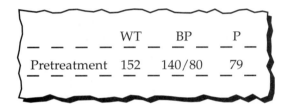

Normal Ranges

Dry Weight: 125
Weight: 125–140
BP: 120/60–130/70
Pulse: 70–80

	WT	BP	P
Pretreatment	152	140/80	79

15. Is any of the data unusual? Explain. **Pretreatment weight and blood pressure higher than normal.**

INSIDE INFORMATION

A registered nurse should:

- be a good listener and have a strong desire to help people
- be able to communicate with different types of people
- work carefully and pay very close attention to detail
- be comfortable around hospitals and people that are ill
- be able to learn how to operate technical equipment
- be able to compute with units of measure in both the U.S. customary system and the metric system

Minimum Education: 2–3 year A.D.N. program, 4–5 year B.S.N. program, or a 2–3 year diploma program

Additional Requirement: Must pass examination to become a registered nurse.

Related Careers: Occupational Therapist, Nurse Practitioner

Starting Salary: $21,580–$29,692

POSTAL CLERK

Julie Dix has been a postal clerk for more than twenty years. She has many different responsibilities. For example, she orders stamps, boxes, and envelopes; weighs and measures packages; and computes the cost of mailing a letter outside the United States. Here is a look at some parts of Julie's job.

CALCULATING SUPPLY QUANTITIES

About every two weeks, the clerks at each window check their stock of stamps. Then they fill out the following Stamp Requisition Form to order stamps.

Complete the form to find the total.

STAMP REQUISITION FORM		
Quantity	Price per Item	Value
Ordinary Postage Stamps		
800	1¢	$ 8.00
1. 1250	3¢	37.50
2. 2500	5¢	125.00
3. 5000	10¢	500.00
Airmail		
4. 1500	46¢	690.00
5. 4000	50¢	2,000.00
Books		
6. 750	$3.30	2,475.00
Coils		
7. 175	$33.00	5,775.00
8. 75	$165.00	12,375.00
Postal Cards		
9. 500	20¢ Regular, Cut	100.00
Stamped Envelopes		
10. 0	No. $6\frac{3}{4}$ – 39¢	0.00
11. 500	No. 10 – 39¢	195.00
Misc.		
12. 50	Inaugural Set – $4.95	247.50
13. REQUISITION TOTAL		$ 24,528.00

DETERMINING MONEY ORDER FEES

Post offices also sell money orders. Postal **money orders** are like bank checks and can be cashed by the company or person to whom they are made out. Post offices charge a small fee for each money order.

Before going to lunch, Julie checks to see how many money orders she has sold. Use the information below to complete the chart that follows.

MONEY ORDER FEES
All money orders, regardless of amount, are now the same price. The price is now $0.80 per money order. This change will affect the problems on page 32.

Determine the fee for each money order. Then find the totals.

MONEY ORDER LIST

01/09/99 Julie Dix

NUMBER	4021492536	4021492537	4021492538	4021492539	4021492540	4021492541	4021492542
14. AMOUNT	$ 28.84	$ 572.81	$ 32.68	$ 48.40	$ 2.44	$ 10.00	$ 36.00
15. FEE	.80	.80	.80	.80	.80	.80	.80
16. TOTAL	$ 29.64	$573.61	$33.48	$49.20	$3.24	$10.80	$36.80

17. What is the total amount (including fees) of money orders purchased by noon? _____$736.77_____

18. A customer asks for a money order in the amount of $11.60. If she gives Julie $20 for the money order and fee, how much change will she receive? _____$7.60_____

19. Mrs. Pitts wants two money orders: one for $19.95 and one for $49.95. What is the total amount of the money orders including the fees? _____$71.50_____

20. Mrs. Pitts gives Julie 4 twenty-dollar bills. How much change will Mrs. Pitts receive? List the fewest number of bills and coins you could give as change.

   $8.50; one $5 bill, three $1 bills, two quarters

CALCULATING DELIVERY CHARGES FOR PARCELS
PARCELS FOR DOMESTIC DELIVERY (Delivery within the United States)

The **length** of a package is the length of its longest sides. The **girth** is the total distance around the package. If the total of the length and the girth is over 130 inches, the package cannot be accepted for delivery in the United States. If the weight is over 70 pounds, it cannot be accepted either. The package shown at right weighs 21 pounds.

Length: 24 in.   Girth: Distance around the parcel.
12 in. + 8 in. + 12 in. + 8 in.

21. Girth: ___40___ in.

22. Length + Girth: ___64___ in.

23. Can Julie accept the package for delivery within the United States? ___yes___

Determine whether the following parcels are acceptable for delivery within the United States.

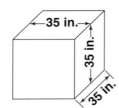

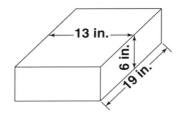

24. Weight: 56 pounds
   Length: ___35 in.___ Girth: ___140 in.___
   Length + Girth: ___175 in.___
   Acceptable? ___no___

25. Weight: 10 pounds
   Length: ___19 in.___ Girth: ___38 in.___
   Length + Girth: ___57 in.___
   Acceptable? ___yes___

Name _____ Class _____ Date _____

POSTAL CLERK

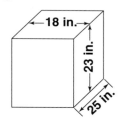

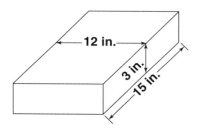

26. Weight: 56 pounds

Length: __25 in.__ Girth: __82 in.__

Length + Girth: __107 in.__

Acceptable? __yes__

27. Weight: 10 pounds

Length: __15 in.__ Girth: __30 in.__

Length + Girth: __45 in.__

Acceptable? __yes__

CALCULATING POSTAGE TO OTHER COUNTRIES

The next customer is someone who has many friends and relatives living in Canada and Mexico. Julie uses the following chart to find the amount of postage for each letter.

Weight Not Over*		Canada	Mexico
(lb)	(oz)		
0	0.5	$0.48	$0.40
0	1.0	0.55	0.46
0	1.5	0.67	0.66
0	2.0	0.76	0.86
0	3.0	1.00	1.26
0	4.0	1.20	1.66
0	5.0	1.40	2.06
0	6.0	1.60	2.46
0	7.0	1.80	2.86
0	8.0	2.00	3.26
0	9.0	2.19	3.66
0	10.0	2.39	4.06
0	11.0	2.59	4.46
0	12.0	2.79	4.86
1	0.0	3.59	6.46
1	8.0	4.52	9.66
2	0.0	5.44	12.86
2	8.0	6.36	16.06
3	0.0	7.29	19.26
3	8.0	8.21	22.46

Find the cost of each letter.

	ADDRESS	WEIGHT	COST
	John McFadden Hotel Reforma Mexico City, Mexico	1 lb 6 oz.	$9.66
28.	Señora Paula Ortiz 28 Calle de Dulce Guanajuato, Mexico	10 oz.	__$4.06__
29.	Danielle DePlan 16049 Avenida de Juarez Juarez, Mexico	3 lbs 8 oz.	__$22.46__
30.	Claude DePlan St. Estephe Hotel Ontario, Canada	2 lbs 10 oz.	__$7.29__

ADDRESS	WEIGHT	COST

31. Señor Juan Roldan
c/o Cecilia Valenzuela
Ojinaga, Mexico — 2 lb 10 oz. — $19.26

32. Victor White
14 Rue Charlemagne
Quebec, Canada — 3 oz. — $1.00

33. Charlou Bonnard
965 Haymarket Square
Montreal, Canada — 12 oz. — $2.79

34. Enrique Cardenas
90 Chapultapec
San Miguel de Allende,
Mexico — 1 lb — $6.46

35. How much will it cost to mail all of the letters in items 28–35? $72.98

INSIDE INFORMATION

A postal clerk should:

- enjoy working with people
- be able to follow directions
- have a good memory

- have a strong knowledge of geography
- be able to read maps and tables
- be able to use basic mathematics

Minimum Education: High-school graduate
   Civil Service Test required
   Note: U.S. citizenship required

Starting Salary: $24,599–$26,063 per year

Related Careers: File Clerk, Routing Clerk

PLUMBER

Orlandis Freeman is a plumbing engineer. He installs plumbing in schools, hospitals, factories, and office buildings. Measuring lengths of pipe, knowing code regulations, drawing plumbing layouts, and pricing the cost of materials are important parts of a plumber's work.

MEASURING THREADED PIPE

Measuring threaded pipe can be done in five different ways.

- End to End:

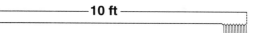

- End to Center:

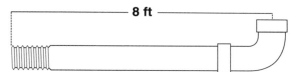

- End to Face:

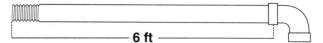

- Face to Face:

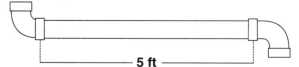

- Center to Center:

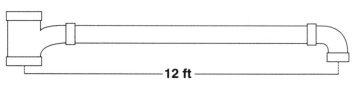

Name the kind of measurement shown in the following drawings.

1. **End to Face** _____

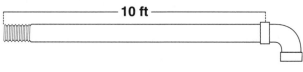

2. **Face to Face** _____

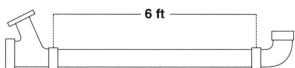

3. **End to End** _____

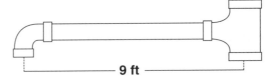

4. **Center to Center** _____

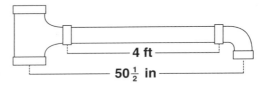

5. What is the CENTER TO CENTER length of the pipe at the right?

    _____50____ in.

6. What is the FACE TO FACE measurement of the pipe at the right?

    _____33____ in.

7. The END TO CENTER length of the pipe at the right is

    _____60____ in.

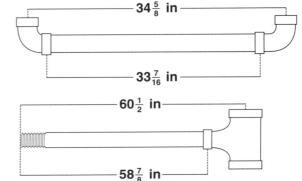

APPLYING CODE REGULATIONS

Like the other building trades, plumbers must follow codes, or guidelines, when installing fixtures. A certain number of fixtures are required in homes, businesses, and schools. Here are some of the regulations for the city where Orlandis works. In the table below, _lavatory_ means toilet.

LAVATORIES FOR EMPLOYEES IN OFFICE BUILDINGS			
Number of Employees	Number of Lavatories Required	Number of Employees	Number of Lavatories Required
1 – 20	1	81 – 100	5
21 – 40	2	101 – 125	6
41 – 60	3	126 – 150	7
61 – 80	4	151 – 175*	8

*When the number of employees is greater than 175, add 1 lavatory for every 30 employees over 175.

- LAVATORIES IN SCHOOLS: 1 lavatory for each 50 pupils

- LAVATORIES FOR MOTION PICTURE PROJECTION BOOTHS:
  If booth has more than one projector, there should be one lavatory on the same level no more than 20 feet away.

- DRINKING FOUNTAINS IN OFFICE BUILDINGS/FACTORIES:
  1 fountain for each 75 employees

- DRINKING FOUNTAINS IN SCHOOLS:
  1 fountain for each 150 pupils, with at least 1 fountain on each floor where there are classrooms.

Refer to the codes above to answer the following questions.

8. Abingdon Middle School has 2700 students. How many drinking fountains is the school required to have?   _____18_____

9. How many lavatories should Abingdon Middle School have?   _____54_____

PLUMBER

10. The Can Do Canning Company employs 92 people. What is the least number of lavatories their building must contain?

_5_

11. The American Trust Company's building has 48 drinking fountains. Estimate the number of employees that work in the building.

_3,600_

12. Explain how you made your estimate for Exercise 11.

__I assumed that enough drinking fountains were installed to meet the requirement.__

__I multiplied 48 by 75.__

13. The Happy Feet Shoe Company is building a new factory. The company employs 325 people. How many lavatories must be installed?

_13_

14. Cinema 20 has 3 projectors in one of its booths. The lavatory is 30 feet away. What regulation is being broken?

__With more than 1 projector, there should be 1 lavatory no more than 20 feet away.__

15. The Palace Theater has 1 projector in its booth. Is there a requirement for the location of a lavatory?

_No_

16. The Bubbly Bottling Company employs 265 people. The plant has 13 lavatories for the employees. Is this figure greater than or less than the number of lavatories required?

Greater than

DETERMINING MATERIALS COST

Orlandis's last job was installing the plumbing in a huge convention center. On large jobs such as this, the plumber receives a set of drawings from the architect and the engineer. The drawings show where pipes and fixtures are to be placed. Orlandis uses these drawings to help him determine the cost of the job.

The diagram to the right shows the drawing for one small part of the plumbing at the convention center.

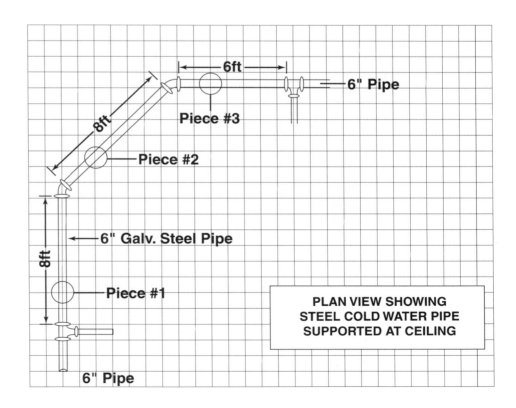

PLAN VIEW SHOWING
STEEL COLD WATER PIPE
SUPPORTED AT CEILING

Refer to the diagram at the bottom of page 37 to complete the table of costs.

COST OF MATERIALS

PIPE

Piece #	Quantity Needed	Unit Price	Total Price
1	8 ft	$35 per ft	$280.00
17. 2	8 ft	$35 per ft	$280.00
18. 3	6 ft	$35 per ft	$210.00

FITTINGS (45 ELL and TEE are fittings that join pipes together.)

19. 45 ELL	2	$56.35 ea.	$112.70
20. TEE	2	$92.00 ea.	$184.00
21. TOTAL (PIPE AND FITTINGS)			$1,066.70

INSIDE INFORMATION

A plumber should:

- be able to read and make technical and scale drawings
- know the plumbing codes and safety regulations in his or her community
- enjoy taking apart objects, figuring out how they work, and putting them back together
- be strong enough to carry and install heavy pipes
- know how to use a calculator

Minimum Education: High-school graduate, apprenticeship with plumber
College-level courses in engineering are helpful.

Starting salary: $21,372–$27,000

Related Careers: Plumber Assistant, Pipefitter

DENTAL ASSISTANT

Debby Ashford works in a busy office with Dr. Taylor, a dentist. She schedules appointments, keeps track of patient billing, and assists Dr. Taylor when he performs various procedures.

WORKING WITH TIME INTERVALS

On Monday morning, the office opens at 7:00 A.M. At that time, patients are calling to schedule appointments.

Here is a section of Dr. Taylor's appointment schedule for the week.

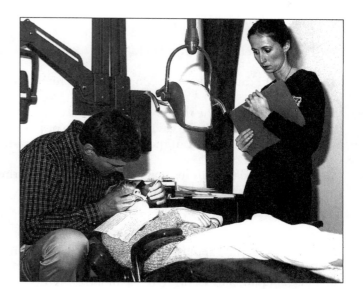

	Monday June 3	Tuesday June 4	Wednesday June 5	Thursday June 6	Friday June 7
11:30	Jones	Hernandez	Miller		O
11:45					F
12:00	↓		↓		F
12:15	Williams	↓	Watkins	Rivera	I
12:30	↓	Rycroft		↓	C
12:45	**Martin**				E
1:00	↓	↓	↓		
1:15	**O'Connor**	Edwards	**Dodd**		C
1:30					O
1:45		↓			S
2:00		Scofield	Murphy		S
2:15		↓			E
2:30		Hall	↓	Kaplan	D
2:45			Clark	↓	
3:00		↓		↓	

Ms. Martin is the first to call. She has broken a tooth and wants to schedule an appointment for the earliest possible date. She can't see the dentist before 11:30 and can't stay later than 3:00. You know the dentist needs at least 30 minutes to examine a patient and take X rays, if necessary.

1. What is the earliest day and time you have for Ms. Martin's appointment? Write her appointment on the schedule. Use an arrow to show when the appointment ends.

Mr. Dodd calls. It's time for his annual checkup and cleaning. A checkup examination and X rays take a half hour. A cleaning takes 15 minutes.

2. How much time will Mr. Dodd's visit require? _____ 45 minutes _____

3. Mr. Dodd can't make it on Monday. Write him in for the next available appointment.

Mrs. O'Connor calls. She thinks she has a cavity in a lower molar. Dr. Taylor will have to examine the tooth and take X rays. If the cavity is very large or painful, he may decide to fill it immediately. A filling usually takes 45 minutes, but the doctor needs an extra 15 minutes for a complicated filling.

4. List all of the procedures that may be performed during Mrs. O'Connor's visit and how much time they require. _____ Exam and X rays—30 minutes _____

   Filling—60 min. _____

5. How much time should you allow for Mrs. O'Connor's visit? _____ 1 hours, or 90 minutes _____

6. She's in pain and wants to come in today. Write her appointment into the schedule.

COMPUTING PATIENT ACCOUNTS

Debby keeps track of each patient's account. Sometimes the patient pays the entire bill at once. Other times, the patient prefers to break it up into several payments. In many cases, the patient's insurance pays a percentage of the cost of dental work.

After Dr. Taylor examines the patient, he decides what procedures must be performed and writes a cost estimate for the patient. Here is a list of some common dental procedures and what they might cost.

Major Dentistry	
Complete Dentures	$3,500
Partial Dentures/Bridge	$1,750
Porcelain Crown	$ 600
Basic Dentistry	
Composite (filling)	$ 70
Extraction (tooth removal)	$ 90
Root Canal Therapy	$ 500
Preventive Dentistry	
Checkup Examination	$ 25
X ray (6–8)	$ 75
X ray (full set, 14–16)	$ 100
Prophylaxis (cleaning)	$ 50
Fluoride Treatment	$ 65

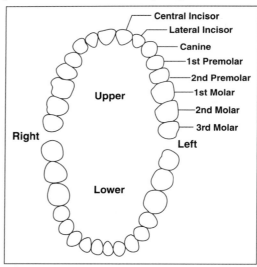

Mrs. O'Connor didn't need X rays after all. Dr. Taylor examined her tooth and filled the cavity. He also gave her a checkup examination and cleaned her teeth.

7. Using the chart, find Mrs. O'Connor's total bill. _____ $145 _____

Mr. Dodd had a checkup examination, a cleaning, and a fluoride treatment. The checkup included a full set of X rays.

8. What is Mr. Dodd's total bill? _____ $240 _____

Dental Assistant

9. Mr. Dodd pays his bill but his insurance will pay the first $150 of the bill. How much of the total bill will Mr. Dodd end up paying? _____$90_____

Ms. Martin needs a porcelain crown to replace her broken tooth. The entire procedure requires four visits. Today, she had an examination and 6 X rays. Her fourth visit will include a cleaning.

10. What is Ms. Martin's total bill? _____$750_____

11. Ms. Martin wants to pay part of her bill during each visit. The last payment will be made on the day the treatment is completed. She agreed to pay the same amount each visit. How much will each payment be? _____$187.50_____

Complete the form below for Ms. Martin's account. She visited the dentist every Monday. Her first visit was March 3rd. She paid the amounts she agreed to pay on each visit.

Amount of Contract _____$750_____   Amount Promised   ☑ Per Visit

$ _____$187.50_____   ☐

☐ Weekly

☐

In Account With _____

	Date	Amt. Paid		Bal. Due		Date	Amt. Paid		Bal. Due	
12.	6-3	187	50	562	50					
13.	6-10	187	50	375	00					
14.	6-17	187	50	187	50					
15.	6-24	187	50	0						

16. On what date was Ms. Martin's bill paid in full? _____June 24_____

17. Ms. Martin's insurance will pay the first $500 of her dental costs. How much of the total bill will Ms. Martin end up paying? _____$250_____

CALCULATING PROPORTIONS

Ms. Martin's broken tooth was repaired with a porcelain crown. Dr. Taylor uses a dental mold filled with dental cement called **alginate** to make an impression of the broken tooth. The impression shows him how large the crown should be.

Debby mixes the alginate in the mold. The amount of alginate she makes depends on the size of the mold. The alginate mixture consists of 2 parts alginate powder and 1 part water. How much water would you add to the following measures of alginate?

	Alginate	Water		Alginate	Water
18.	2 cups	1 cup	21.	$\frac{2}{3}$ cup	$\frac{1}{3}$ cup
19.	1 cup	$\frac{1}{2}$ cup	22.	3 cups	$1\frac{1}{2}$ cups
20.	$\frac{1}{2}$ cup	$\frac{1}{4}$ cup	23.	$2\frac{1}{2}$ cups	$1\frac{1}{4}$ cups

DETERMINING SUPPLY AMOUNTS

The dental assistant is responsible for maintaining the stock of dental supplies. This includes the compounds used for fillings, adhesives and cements such as alginate, and a ready supply of new instruments.

Alginate powder comes in 32-ounce cans. The dentist uses about 64 ounces each week.

24. How many cans of alginate does the dentist use in a week? _____2 cans_____

25. How long will six cans of alginate last? _____3 weeks_____

26. How many cups are in a can of alginate? _____4 cups_____

27. How many cups of alginate does the dentist use in a week? _____8 cups_____

28. If a standard-size mold requires two cups of alginate, how many standard-size molds can be made using one can of alginate? _____2 molds_____

Assume today is Monday, June 10. Debby has four cans of alginate in the storeroom. It takes one week from the day she orders for the alginate to be delivered.

29. What is the latest date she can place an order so that she doesn't run out of alginate? _____June 17th_____

30. Assume there are four weeks in a month. How many cans of alginate will she need for a two-month supply? _____16 cans_____

INSIDE INFORMATION

A dental assistant should:

- know the names and locations of the various kinds of teeth
- understand the various treatments in dentistry
- know how to compute with fractions, percents, and units of measurement
- be calm and ready to reassure patients
- be friendly and cheerful
- be organized and work accurately
- perform many different duties at the same time

Minimum Education: High-school graduate. At least six months of specialized training

Starting Salary: $8–$11 an hour

Related Careers: Medical Assistant, Occupational Therapy Assistant

UNIT 2

Using Ratio, Proportion, and Percent

UNIT 2

Using Ratio, Proportion, and Percent

INTERIOR DESIGNER

Patricia Barron is an interior designer. She often works with an architect. Together they plan the layout, furniture, fabrics, and colors for offices of banks, advertising agencies, and law firms. Mathematics is an important part of Patricia's work, particularly when she reads and makes scale drawings.

USING SCALE DRAWINGS

Before you can read or make a scale drawing, there are two important skills you have to master: reading a ruler and writing and solving proportions.

Use a ruler. Measure each line segment to the nearest $\frac{1}{8}$ inch.

1. _____ $\frac{1}{2}$ in.

2. _____ $2\frac{3}{4}$ in.

3. _____ $4\frac{1}{4}$ in.

4. ___ $\frac{1}{4}$ in.

5. _____ $5\frac{3}{8}$ in.

Draw a line segment of the given length. Label your drawings.

6. 2 in.

7. $1\frac{1}{2}$ in.

8. $4\frac{1}{4}$ in.   **Check students' drawings.**

9. $\frac{3}{4}$ in.

10. $5\frac{3}{4}$ in.

SOLVING PROPORTIONS

When working with scale drawings, designers are faced with one of two situations. They have to calculate the actual length of an object, given the length on the scale drawing. Or, they know the actual length of an object, and they have to figure out the corresponding length on the scale drawing. In either case, designers have to know how to solve proportions. Follow these steps to solve a proportion.

Example: Solve. $\frac{6}{10} = \frac{n}{35}$

- Multiply to find cross products
$$6 \times 35 = 10 \times n$$
$$210 = 10 \times n$$

- Divide to find n.
$$210 \div 10 = n$$
$$21 = n$$

- Check by finding cross products.
$$\frac{6}{10} \overset{?}{=} \frac{21}{35}$$
$$6 \times 35 \overset{?}{=} 10 \times 21$$
$$210 = 210 \checkmark$$

Solve the proportion. Follow the steps above.

11. $\frac{8}{20} = \frac{n}{25}$ _____ $n = 10$

12. $\frac{n}{50} = \frac{72}{75}$ _____ $n = 48$

13. $\frac{21}{28} = \frac{6}{n}$ _____ $n = 8$

14. $\frac{13}{n} = \frac{65}{115}$ _____ $n = 23$

15. $\frac{12}{4} = \frac{15}{n}$ _____ $n = 5$

16. $\frac{n}{11.4} = \frac{6}{12}$ _____ $n = 5.7$

17. $\frac{n}{519} = \frac{3}{173}$ _____ $n = 9$

18. $\frac{n}{3.6} = \frac{60}{80}$ _____ $n = 2.7$

INTERPRETING SCALE DRAWINGS

Now that you've practiced these basic skills, you're ready to tackle the work of an interior designer.

This scale drawing is for one of the offices that Patricia is designing. Patricia has made this drawing to help her client decide what type of furniture should be in the office and where it should be placed. This drawing shows the **plan view,** or the **top view,** of the office. It's as if you are looking down at the office from the middle of the ceiling.

Study the scale drawing.

19. How many chairs are planned for this office? _____ 4

20. How many small round tables will be in this office?

_____ 1 _____

21. What piece of furniture will be along the north wall?

_____ table _____

22. What type of furniture will be along the west wall?

_____ bookcase _____

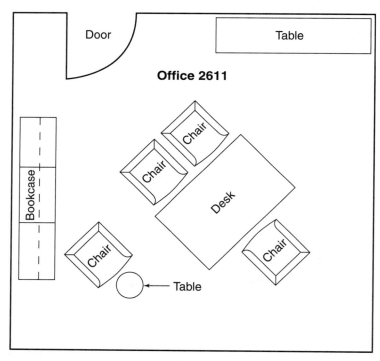

46

INTERIOR DESIGNER

23. Is the executive in this office more likely to sit on the east or the west side of the desk? _____ **east** _____

In the exercises below, *length* means the distance of the longest side. *Width* means the distance of the shortest side.

Use a ruler. Measure the following distances on the scale, drawing to the nearest $\frac{1}{8}$ inch.

24. the length of the east wall _____ $3\frac{5}{8}$ **in.** _____

25. the length of the south wall _____ $3\frac{3}{4}$ **in.** _____

26. the length of the desk _____ $1\frac{1}{4}$ **in.** _____

27. the width of the desk _____ $\frac{3}{4}$ **in.** _____

28. the width of one of the small chairs on the west side of the desk _____ $\frac{1}{2}$ **in.** _____

29. the length of the same chair _____ $\frac{1}{2}$ **in.** _____

30. the width of the door _____ $\frac{3}{4}$ **in.** _____

31. the length of the north wall minus the width of the door _____ **3 in.** _____

In this drawing, Patricia used the scale of $\frac{1}{4}$ in. = 1 ft. This means that each distance of $\frac{1}{4}$ in. on the drawing stands for a length of 1 foot of the full-sized object. To calculate the actual length of an object from this scale drawing, you need to write and solve a proportion.

Example: What is the actual length (in feet) of the east wall?

STEP 1: Write a proportion.

Drawing length (in.) $\longrightarrow$ $\dfrac{\frac{1}{4}}{1} = \dfrac{3\frac{5}{8}}{n}$
Actual length (ft) $\longrightarrow$

STEP 2: Solve the proportion.

$\frac{1}{4} \times n = 1 \times 3\frac{5}{8}$

$\frac{1}{4} \times n = 1 \times \frac{29}{8}$

$n = \frac{29}{8} \div \frac{1}{4}$

$n = 14\frac{1}{2}$

The actual length of the east wall is $14\frac{1}{2}$ ft.

Calculate the actual distance.

32. the length of the west wall _____ $14\frac{1}{2}$ **ft** _____

33. the length of the south wall _____ **15 ft** _____

34. the length of the bookcase on the west wall _____ **7 ft** _____

35. the width of the door _____ **3 ft** _____

36. the length of one of the chairs at the desk _____ **2 ft** _____

37. the length of the desk _____ **5 ft** _____

CREATING A SCALE DRAWING

Patricia needs some help. She wants you to make a scale drawing of the layout for Office 2620. The client wants the same furniture and layout as in Office 2611. The only difference is that Office 2620 is larger. The walls are 20 ft by 20 ft.

38. Begin your scale drawing by drawing the walls first. Write and solve a proportion to determine the length each wall should be on the drawing. Don't forget to include a door on the north wall.

Example: East Wall

Drawing length (in.) ⟶ $\dfrac{1}{4} = \dfrac{n}{20}$

Actual length (ft) ⟶ $\dfrac{1}{4} \times 20 = n \times 1$

$5 = n$ The drawing length of the east wall should be 5 in.

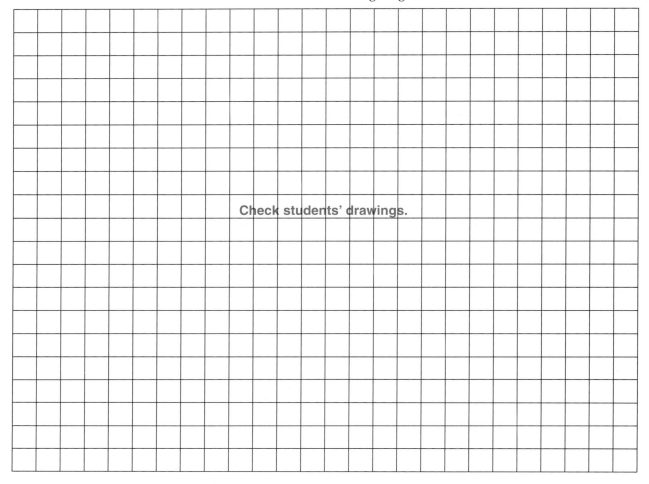

Check students' drawings.

39. Complete the drawing by showing the furniture. Use the same furniture as in Office 2611.

You're off to a good start. If you want more experience, think about redecorating your bedroom. In addition to making a scale drawing, you could also make a budget for how much you can spend on furniture, curtains, paint, and so on. Good luck!

---

*I*NSIDE *I*NFORMATION

An interior designer should:

- visualize the way a room would look with furniture, carpeting, etc.
- draw well and read and make scale drawings
- like to experiment with colors and fabrics
- be attentive to details
- enjoy meeting and working with a variety of customers

Minimum Education: Bachelor's degree in Interior Design   *Starting Salary:* approximately $27,000 per year

Related Careers: Architect, Interior Decorator, Fashion Designer

PHOTOGRAPHER

Kathy Stevens is a photographer from Colorado who specializes in taking photographs of houses and gardens. She travels often throughout the United States to take pictures for various magazines. Kathy has just finished shooting a series of photographs of a plantation near New Orleans. Her next assignment is in Los Angeles.

PLANNING A PHOTO SHOOT

In Los Angeles, Kathy is scheduled to shoot a house at sunrise. (*Shoot* means to take a series of photographs.) The period of time when the sun first rises is called "the magic hour." That is the best time for taking pictures of the outside of the house. All of the equipment must be set up and ready to use when the sun appears. The weather also plays an important part in setting up the photograph. Is rain expected? Will there be clouds? What will the temperature be?

After she arrives in Los Angeles, Kathy needs to find out the following information about the next day.

- The times of sunrise and sunset
- The weather report

1. What sources would you use to find this information?

   Answers may include newspaper, television, radio, the Internet, and calling

   the telephone number for the weather report.

USING A FLOOR PLAN

Kathy will first take photographs of the outside of the house at dawn. Then she will photograph the inside of the house. She will use sunlight as her major source of light. She studies the floor plan to the right.

These rooms will be photographed.

- Master suite
- Bedroom #3
- Living room
- Family room

Symbols: ▭ Windows   △ Doors

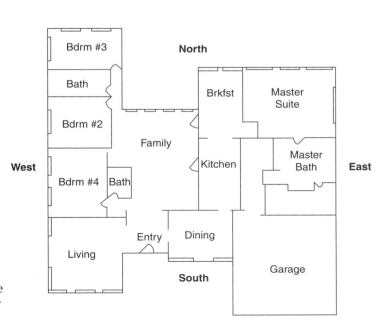

Kathy will allow 2 hours for each room to be photographed. It will take about 1 hour to move the equipment from one room to another. Kathy starts shooting inside the house at 7:30 A.M.

Make a schedule for the rest of the shoot. Remember that the sun rises in the east and sets in the west and that Kathy needs as much light as possible in each room when shooting.

	ROOM	TIME
2.	Master suite	7:30 A.M. – 9:30 A.M.
3.	Family room	10:30 A.M. – 12:30 P.M.
	lunch	12:30 P.M. – 1:30 P.M.
4.	Living room	2:30 P.M. – 4:30 P.M.
5.	Bedroom 3	5:30 P.M. – 7:30 P.M.

USING PROPORTIONS, SIMILAR FIGURES, AND PERCENTAGES

The sun rises on schedule at 6:23 A.M. Kathy is ready and captures the magic hour on film. She then moves her equipment into the house and photographs the rooms according to the schedule she made out the night before. Then she returns to the family room to take the picture that will be on the cover of the magazine.

When Kathy looks through the viewfinder of her 35 mm camera, she sees a rectangular image with sides in the ratio 1:1.5. She knows that the photograph on the cover of the magazine is to be 9 inches by 12 inches. Some of the top of the photo she takes will be cut off so the photo will have the correct shape.

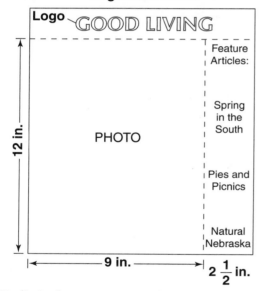

To find what percentage of the image in the viewfinder will fit on the cover, Kathy follows these steps.

STEP 1: Find the length of the image in the camera that corresponds to the length of the photo on the magazine cover. Write and solve a proportion.

	Magazine Cover		Image in Viewfinder
Width (inches)	9	$=$	1
Length (inches)	12		n

$$9 \times n = 12 \times 1$$
$$9n = 12$$
$$9n \div 9 = 12 \div 9$$
$$n \approx 1.33 \qquad \approx \text{means } approximately\ equal\ to$$

Name _____ Class _____ Date _____

PHOTOGRAPHER

The shape of the photo on the cover is to be the same shape as the shaded area of the diagram at the right.

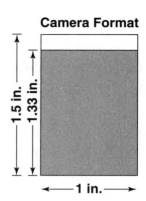

Camera Format

1.5 in.
1.33 in.
1 in.

STEP 2: Find what percentage of the image in the viewfinder will fit on the cover.

Think: What percent of 1.5 is 1.33?

$$1.5 \times n = 1.33$$
$$n = 1.33 \div 1.5$$
$$n = 0.89 \text{ (rounded to the nearest hundredth)}$$

About 89% of the image in the viewfinder will fit on the cover of the magazine.

Suppose now that the magazine editors decided to have a smaller photo on the cover. It will be 8 inches across and 10 inches deep. Repeat steps 1 and 2 to find what percentage of the image in the viewfinder will fit on the cover of the magazine.

STEP 1: Find the length of the image in the camera that corresponds to the length of the photo on the cover. Solve the proportion.

Magazine Cover | Image in Viewfinder

6. Width (inches) $\dfrac{8}{10} = \dfrac{1}{n}$

   Length (inches)

7. Multiply to find cross products. $\underline{8} \times n = \underline{10} \times 1$

8. Multiply on each side of the equation. $\underline{8n} = \underline{10}$

9. Divide to find n. $8n \div \underline{8} = \underline{10} \div \underline{8}$

10. $n = \underline{1.25}$

11. The amount of space available on the cover corresponds to 1 in. by __1.25__ in. of space within the viewfinder.

Camera Format

1.25 in.
1.5 in.

STEP 2: Find what percentage of the image in the viewfinder will fit on the cover.

12. Think: What percent of 1.5 is __1.25__ ?

13. $1.5 \times n = \underline{1.25}$

14. $n = \underline{1.25} \div 1.5$

15. $n = \underline{0.83}$ (rounded to the nearest hundredth)

16. About __83__ % of the image in the viewfinder will fit on the cover of the magazine.

Find what percentage of the image in the viewfinder will fit on the cover of the magazine.

17. The photograph on the cover of *Good Life* magazine will be 10 inches across and 12 inches deep.

    About ___80___ % of the image in the viewfinder will fit on the cover of the magazine.

18. The photograph on the cover of *Teen World* magazine will be 12 inches across and 14 inches deep.

    About ___78___ % of the image in the viewfinder will fit on the cover of the magazine.

19. The photograph on the cover of *Vacation Time* magazine will be 9 inches across and 12 inches deep.

    About ___89___ % of the image in the viewfinder will fit on the cover of the magazine.

20. The photograph on the cover of *TV This Week* will be 5 inches across and 7 inches deep.

    About ___93___ % of the image in the viewfinder will fit on the cover of the magazine.

After Kathy finishes photographing the family room for the cover, she packs up her equipment, gets her luggage, and heads for the airport. Tomorrow, she will be home in Mississippi. Next week, she'll be in France taking pictures of a castle.

INSIDE INFORMATION

A photographer should:

- have a good technical understanding of photography
- be creative
- have good eyesight
- be willing to work odd hours

Minimum Education: College education or other post-secondary training

Starting Salary: $14,000–$21,000 per year

Related Careers: Illustrator, Designer

HOME HEALTH AIDE

Christa Conroy is a home health aide in her hometown of Seattle. She provides personal homecare services to clients who are unable to care for themselves. Her duties range from offering cheerful conversation to assisting with various medical needs. Some of Christa's clients have short-term needs which require her help for only a few days or weeks. Other clients require long-term care of several months to years.

It is important that Christa keeps accurate records of the services she performs, as well as her clients' condition and progress. This way, a supervisor can evaluate Christa's work and help with any concerns or problems that might arise.

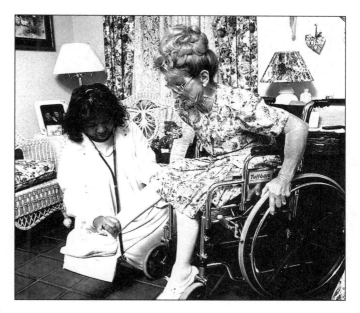

USING PERCENTS AND CIRCLE GRAPHS

A table showing the percentage of time Christa spends per week performing certain activities is shown below.

Activity	Percentage of Time Per Week
Grooming/Dressing Clients	15%
Meal Planning/Cooking	40%
Medical Assistance	5%
Emotional Support/Listening	10%
Record Keeping	10%
Cleaning	20%

Match the letter of the section on the circle graph with the corresponding activity from the table.

1. Cleaning _____B_____

2. Record Keeping _____D or E_____

3. Grooming/Dressing Clients _____C_____

4. Medical Assistance _____F_____

5. Meal Planning/Cooking _____A_____

6. Emotional Support/Listening _____D or E_____

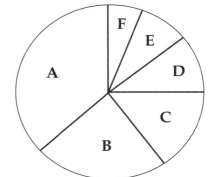

7. Which activity required the greatest percentage of time? Which activity required the least?

   Meal Planning and Cooking required the most time, while Medical Assisting required the least time.

CALCULATING WEEKLY HOURS FROM PERCENTAGES

If Christa worked a total of 42 hours during the week shown by the circle graph in Exercises 1–7, how many hours would each of the percentages represent? Use the percentages given in Exercises 1–7 to calculate your answers in hours and minutes.

Bathing Client   **30% = 42 hours $\times$ .30 = 12.6 hours**

To convert .6 hour to minutes: 60 minutes $\times$ .6 = 36 minutes
Answer: 12 hours 36 minutes

8. Grooming/Dressing Clients   6 hours 18 minutes

9. Meal Planning/Cooking   16 hours 48 minutes

10. Medical Assistance   2 hours 6 minutes

11. Emotional Support/Listening   4 hours 12 minutes

12. Record Keeping   4 hours 12 minutes

13. Cleaning   8 hours 24 minutes

CHANGING PERCENTAGES INTO NUMBERS

Using the same method as above, practice converting percentages to numbers by changing the following percentages of time into hours and minutes.

14. 13% of 40 hours   5 hours 12 minutes   15. 12% of 45 hours   5 hours 24 minutes

16. 38% of 80 hours   30 hours 24 minutes   17. 5% of 40 hours   2 hours

18. 60% of 80 hours   48 hours   19. 75% of 42 hours   31 hours 30 minutes

WRITING PERCENTS FROM FRACTIONS

During the course of one day, Christa recorded the following activities. She worked a total of 12 hours including transit time and a lunch break. In the table on page 55, express each activity as a fraction of the total weekly hours, then write the fraction as a percentage.

Time	Activity
8:00 A.M. – 10:00 A.M.	Cleaned house at Mrs. Brown's.
10:00 A.M. – 10:30 A.M.	Bathed and dressed Mrs. Brown.
10:30 A.M. – 11:30 A.M.	Prepared lunch and dinner for Mrs. Brown.
11:30 A.M. – 1:00 P.M	Sat outside and chatted with Mrs. Brown.
1:00 P.M – 2:00 P.M	Drove to Mr. Chandler's house, stopped for lunch.
2:00 P.M – 3:00 P.M	Helped Mr. Chandler with back brace and changed medical dressings.
3:00 P.M – 4:00 P.M	Prepared Mr. Chandler's dinner and snacks.
4:00 P.M – 5:00 P.M	Played cards with Mr. Chandler.
5:00 P.M – 7:00 P.M	Cleaned and did laundry.
7:00 P.M – 7:30 P.M	Ate dinner with Mr. Chandler.
7:30 P.M – 8:00 P.M.	Dressed Mr. Chandler for bed.

HOME HEALTH AIDE

Total Hours: 12

Activity	Fraction of Total Hours	Percentage
20. Cleaning	$\frac{4}{12}$	33%
21. Record Keeping	none	0%
22. Grooming/Dressing Clients	$\frac{1}{12}$	8%
23. Medical Assistance	$\frac{1}{12}$	8%
24. Meal Planning/Cooking	$\frac{2}{12}$	17%
25. Emotional Support/Listening	$\frac{3}{12}$	25%
26. Transit Time/Lunch Break	$\frac{1}{12}$	8%

CREATING A CIRCLE GRAPH FROM PERCENTAGES

27. Using the percentages in Exercises 20–26, fill in the empty circle below to create a circle graph representing Christa's activity percentages.

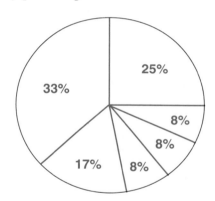

Use the information from the above exercises to answer the questions.

28. Did Christa spend a greater percentage of time Meal Planning during the single day or during the entire week?

    Christa spent 40% of her week Meal Planning and Cooking and only 17% in the single day.

29. Of both the daily and weekly percentages, in which activity did Christa spend the least amount of time?

The least amount of time was spent in Medical Assistance—5%.

30. How might you label the two circle graphs to best describe what they represent?

One graph could be labeled, "Home Health Aide Activities for One Week" and the other

could be labeled, "Home Health Aide Activities for One Day."

COMPARING PERCENTAGES

Below is a record of Christa's activities for four weeks. Study the information carefully, then answer the questions.

Activity	Week 1	Week 2	Week 3	Week 4
Medical Assistance	11 hrs.	13 hrs.	7 hrs.	7 hrs.
Cleaning	10 hrs.	10 hrs.	15 hrs.	11 hrs.
Emotional Support	4 hrs.	5 hrs.	7 hrs.	8 hrs.
Meal Planning	8 hrs.	7 hrs.	5 hrs.	7 hrs.
Grooming/Dressing	2 hrs.	1 hr.	1 hr.	2 hrs.
Transit Time	4 hrs.	3 hrs.	4 hrs.	4 hrs.
Record Keeping	1 hr.	1 hr.	1 hr.	1 hr.

31. How many hours per week did Christa work during this four-week period? ___40 hours___

32. What combined percentage of time did Christa spend in Cleaning and Meal Planning for each of the four weeks?

For Week 1—18 hours or 45%; Week 2—17 hours or 42.5%; Week 3—20 hours or 50%;

Week 4—18 hours or 45%

33. For the entire four-week period, what percentage of time is spent in Transit Time? Show your work.

The four-week period represents 160 hours of time. The total time spent over four weeks

in Transit Time is 15 hours. This represents 9% of 160 hours.

INSIDE INFORMATION

A home health aide should:

- have good record keeping skills
- have good writing and communication skills
- enjoy helping people

- be responsible and compassionate
- be able to read and record vital signs

Minimum Education: Most states require no formal training. A competency test is required by federal law.

Starting Salary: $5.96–$8.29 per hour

Related Careers: Physical Therapy Aide, Nursery School Attendant

CUSTOMER SERVICE REPRESENTATIVE

A large computer company has a toll-free number for customers who want to order supplies over the telephone. Kevin Mah is the manager of this department. He supervises 12 customer service representatives who process telephone and mail orders.

PROCESSING CUSTOMERS' ORDERS WITH PERCENTAGES

The customer service representatives enter customers' orders directly into a computer system. They also process anywhere from 20 to 40 mail orders each day.

In addition to the prices of supplies, there are other charges or discounts the representatives must be aware of:

- A C.O.D. (cash on delivery) charge of $1.85 for every order
- State sales tax (CA—6%, IL—6.25%, NV—4.25%, TX—6%)
- A 5% discount on credit card purchases
- A 2% shipping charge on the total dollar amount of computer paper ordered

Complete the following form for a telephone order. Round to the nearest cent.

Ship to: Daniel Ochoa, C.P.A   Acct #: 003–4901
          1803 Piedmont Way   Date: March 24, 1999
          Austin, TX 78714   Payment: American Express

	ITEM	QUANTITY	UNIT PRICE	AMOUNT
1.	#A403 Black Printer Cartridges	8	$6.95	$ 55.60
2.	#A412 Color Printer Cartridges	5	$10.95	$ 54.75
3.	#J191 Ribbons—Comp (JB–1800)	20	$12.00	$ 240.00
4.	#P036 Paper—Comp	12 boxes	$4.96	$ 59.52
5.	TOTAL AMOUNT OF SUPPLIES			$ 409.87
6.	CHARGES: State Tax (6.00%)		$ 24.59	
	Shipping Charge*		$ 1.19	
	Total Amount of Charges			$ 25.78
7.	DISCOUNTS: Credit Card (5% of Total Amount of Supplies)			– (20.49)
8.	TOTAL AMOUNT OF ORDER			$ 415.16

*Additional shipping charge of 2% on total paper order. Minimum order of 2 boxes.

Orders are sent out with a prepaid postcard so customers may request a supply catalog. Sometimes there are price changes, and customers who have ordered supplies by mail must be notified. A customer may either approve the new price or cancel the order. The customer service representative makes a note of this on the order form. Several price changes have recently gone into effect.

Items	Old Price	New Price
#A511 Color Printer Cartridge	$10.95	$12.00
#C005 Ribbons—Type	$ 4.75	$ 5.25
#JK–90 Ribbons—Comp	$14.50	$13.50
#PO46 Paper—Comp	$ 5.25/box	$ 4.25/box
#SV–525 Diskettes	$ 7.50/box	$ 7.75/box

9. Which items have new prices that are less than their old prices?

#JK–90 Ribbons–Comp; #PO46 Paper–Comp

10. By how much has the cost of the Color Printer Cartridge increased?

$1.05

11. A customer mailed in an order for diskettes in the amount of $112.50. The new price total of the diskettes is $116.25. How many boxes of diskettes did the customer order?

15 Boxes

12. A customer mailed in an order for 28 #C005 typewriter ribbons at the old price. By how much has the total amount of the order increased?

$14 ($.50 per ribbon)

Use the above information on price changes to correct the mail-order form shown below.

Ship to: Cara's Quick Copy
92 Alguno Way
El Cerrito, CA 94556

Acct #: 946–1009
Date: April 12, 1999
Payment: C.O.D.

ITEM	QUANTITY	UNIT PRICE (Old)	(New)	AMOUNT	
13. #C005 Ribbons—Type	8	$ 4.75	$ 5.25	$ 42.00	CANCEL
14. #JK–90 Ribbons—Comp	11	$14.50	$ 13.50	$ 148.50	OK
15. #J191 Ribbons—Comp	20	$12.00	$12.00	$ 240.00	SAME
16. #P046 Paper—Comp	12 boxes	$5.25	$ 4.25	$ 51.00	OK
17. #SV–525 Diskettes	32 boxes	$ 7.50	$ 7.75	$ 248.00	OK
18. TOTAL AMOUNT OF SUPPLIES				$ 729.50	

19. CHARGES   State Tax (6.00%) $ 43.77

C.O.D. Charge $ 1.85

Shipping Charge* $ 2.22

Total Amount of Charges $ 47.84

20. DISCOUNTS: Credit Card (5% of Total Amount of Supplies) $(0.00)

21. TOTAL AMOUNT OF ORDER $ 777.34

* Additional shipping charge of 2% on total paper order. Minimum order of 2 boxes.

CUSTOMER SERVICE REPRESENTATIVE

TABULATING DAILY CALL REPORTS

Before setting up the telephone lines in Kevin's department, the company estimated that an average of 2,000 calls would come in every day. They also estimated that each call would last approximately 2 minutes. Here is how they estimated how many customer service representatives they would need.

- A customer service representative who works the telephone a total of 6 hours, or 360 minutes, every day can handle about 180 orders. This is shown below.

  Number of minutes worked ÷ Length of each call = Number of orders

  $$360 \div 2 = 180$$

- The department needs at least 12 customer service representatives to handle 2,000 calls. This is shown below.

  Number of calls ÷ Number of orders per representative = Number of representatives

  $$2,000 \div 180 = 11.11 \approx 12$$

Every day, Kevin receives reports on the previous day's calls. These reports help the company make sure that their estimates of the length of the calls and the number of representatives needed continue to be correct. For instance, adding supplies to the catalog may increase the length of the average call. The company may then need to hire more representatives.

One report lists the number of calls each operator handled, plus the length of each call. A partial report on Beverly Lewis is given below.

22. What was the total amount in minutes of the 10 calls?

    __**39.67 minutes**__

Operator: Beverly Lewis		
Date:	March 23, 1999	
1	2.05	minutes
2	4.36	minutes
3	1.90	minutes
4	3.42	minutes
5	10.16	minutes
6	2.50	minutes
7	2.32	minutes
8	6.16	minutes
9	4.00	minutes
10	2.80	minutes

23. What was the average length of a call? Round to the nearest hundredth.

    __**3.97 minutes**__

24. Find the average length of Beverly's calls if you throw out the longest call. (Hint: you can begin by subtracting the length of the longest call from the total number of minutes.)

    __**3.28 minutes**__

25. Does throwing out the longest call affect Beverly's average? If the longest call isn't included, by how much is Beverly over or under the 2-minute call estimate?

    __**Yes. Beverly is 1.28 minutes over the estimate.**__

26. What do you think happened to make call #5 last more than 10 minutes?

    __**Answers will vary but may include new prices, a problem with an order received, or not**__

    __**knowing the name or number of item.**__

CALCULATING SALARIES

Kevin's department is staffed with both full-time and part-time customer service representatives.

- A full-time representative works 40 hours a week.
- A part-time representative averages 20 hours a week.
- All representatives are paid an hourly rate.
- One hour for lunch is deducted. For example, an 8 A.M. to 5 P.M. workday consists of 8 work hours.
- An employee earns *time and a half* for any hours over 40 hours per week. (*Time and a half* means $1\frac{1}{2}$ times their regular rate.)

Time cards are filled out on Friday and turned in to Kevin. He reviews the cards for accuracy. When Kevin reviewed the following time card, he found 3 errors.

Name: Jason Colari		SS#: 010-02-0304
Monday (March 20)	9:30 A.M. – 5:30 P.M.	7.0 hours
Tuesday (March 21)	8:30 A.M. – 5:30 P.M.	9.0 hours
Wednesday (March 22)	9:00 A.M. – 5:00 P.M.	7.0 hours
Thursday (March 23)	8:00 A.M. – 6:00 P.M.	8.0 hours
Friday (March 24)	9:00 A.M. – 5:00 P.M.	8.0 hours

TOTAL HOURS FOR THE WEEK: _____ hours

Regular:
40 hours × $9.50/hour _____
Overtime:
_____ hours × $14.25/hour _____

TOTAL EARNINGS FOR THE WEEK _____

Review the time card. Find and correct the 3 errors in the number of hours worked:

27. Day __Tuesday, March 21__   Correction __8 hours__

28. Day __Thursday, March 23__   Correction __9 hours__

29. Day __Friday, March 24__   Correction __7 hours__

30. Calculate Jason's total earnings for the week. __$361.00__

INSIDE INFORMATION

A customer service representative should:

- have good communications skills
- have good basic math skills
- enjoy working with people
- be detail-oriented
- have computer skills

Minimum Education: High-school graduate   *Starting Salary:* $15,620–$18,564 per year

Related Careers: Sales Representative, Billing Clerk

TRAVEL AGENT

Susan Jiminez is a travel agent. She specializes in planning cruises for her customers. Here is a situation she faces regularly. Mrs. Domingo says that she would like to take a cruise with her husband. But she hasn't told Susan where she wants to go, when she wants to go, or how much money she wants to spend. Before you can plan a vacation for her, you need more information.

Write the questions you would ask Mrs. Domingo.

1. ____Answers will vary. Sample answers include:_____

2. ____How much money does Mrs. Domingo want to spend?_____

3. ____When would she like to go?_____

4. ____How long would she like to be on a cruise?_____

5. ____Where would she like to go?_____

Assume that Mrs. Domingo gives you the following information:

Home city: *Minneapolis*	Number of people traveling: *2 adults*
Time of trip: *February*	Type of cruise: *7-day Caribbean*
Amount she wants to spend per person: *$1600*	

As the travel agent you need to prepare an itinerary (travel schedule) and give the estimated costs. Follow these steps.

UNDERSTANDING A CRUISE ITINERARY

7-DAY CARIBBEAN CRUISE			
Day	Port	Arrive	Depart
Sun.	Miami, FL		5:00 P.M.
Mon.	At Sea	Cruising to Mexico	
Tues.	Cozumel, Mexico	9:30 A.M.	5:30 P.M.
Wed.	Grand Cayman Island	Noon	6:00 P.M.
Thurs.	Jamaica	8:30 A.M.	4:00 P.M.
Fri.	Haiti	9:00 A.M.	5:00 P.M.
Sat.	At Sea	Cruising to Florida	
Sun.	Miami, FL	8:30 A.M.	

Use the itinerary to answer the following questions:

6. In which city does the cruise begin and end? _____Miami_____

7. On which day and at which time does the cruise depart from Miami? _____Sunday at 5:00 P.M._____

8. Where will the ship be on Thursday? _____Jamaica_____

9. On which day will the ship be in Mexico? _____Tuesday_____

10. On which day and at what time does the ship arrive in Haiti? <u>Friday at 9:00 A.M.</u>

11. Where will the ship be on Saturday? <u>At sea</u>

12. At what time does the ship arrive back in Miami? <u>8:30 A.M.</u>

13. Draw the route of the cruise ship on the map below. Use arrows to show the direction of the route.

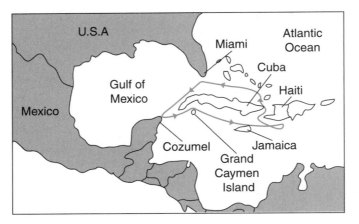

COMPARING DATES AND SEASONS

SAILING DATES: 7-DAY CRUISES							
Value Season						Peak Season	
Jan. 2	May 7	June 25	Aug. 13	Oct. 1	Nov. 12	Jan. 15	Mar. 5
Jan. 8	May 14	July 2	Aug. 20	Oct. 8	Nov. 19	Jan. 22	Mar. 12
Apr. 2	May 21	July 9	Aug. 27	Oct. 15	Nov. 26	Jan 29	Mar. 19
Apr. 9	May 28	July 16	Sept. 3	Oct. 22	Dec. 3	Feb. 5	Mar. 26
Apr. 16	June 4	July 23	Sept. 10	Oct. 29	Dec. 10	Feb. 12	Dec. 24
Apr. 23	June 11	July 30	Sept. 17	Nov. 5	Dec. 17	Feb. 19	Dec. 31
Apr. 30	June 18	Aug. 6	Sept. 24			Feb. 26	

14. Check the sailing dates. Is February part of the Value Season or the Peak Season?

<u>Peak Season</u>

15. The Domingos want to travel in February. On which dates can the Domingos choose to begin their cruise?

<u>Feb. 5, 12, 19, or 26</u>

The prices shown in the table below include round-trip flights to Miami from most major cities throughout North America. Rates shown are per person, assuming two people share a stateroom. The price also includes all meals aboard the ship.

FARES FOR A 7-DAY CRUISE		
Cabin Categories*	Value Season	Peak Season
A Promenade Deck–deluxe large outside stateroom	$1,960	$2,045
B Upper Deck–large outside stateroom	$1,750	$1,825
C Upper Deck–outside stateroom	$1,655	$1,740
D Cabaret Deck–outside stateroom	$1,655	$1,740
E Main Deck–outside stateroom	$1,630	$1,715
F "A" Deck–outside stateroom	$1,555	$1,640
G Upper Deck–inside stateroom	$1,490	$1,575
H Cabaret Deck–inside stateroom	$1,490	$1,575
I "B" Deck–outside stateroom	$1,495	$1,580
J Main Deck–inside stateroom	$1,465	$1,550
K "A" Deck–inside stateroom	$1,410	$1,495
* An outside stateroom has a window or a porthole. An inside stateroom has neither a window nor a porthole.		

16. Will the Domingos be traveling during the Peak Season or the Value Season? _____Peak Season_____

17. In which column should you look to find the cost of their cabin? _____Peak Season_____

18. What is the price per person of the stateroom that comes closest to, but is not above, the $1600 per person that Mrs. Domingo wants to spend? _____$1,580_____

19. Describe the kind of cabin Mr. and Mrs. Domingo will have on the ship.

_____A cabin on "B" deck that will have a window or porthole._____

20. Why do you think rates are cheaper during the Value Season? _____Sample answer: Fewer people_____

_____travel to the Caribbean during the months of warm weather._____

UNDERSTANDING FLIGHT SCHEDULES

Keep these facts in mind when choosing the best flight from Minneapolis to Miami.

- Passengers may begin boarding the ship at 12:30 P.M.
- Everyone must be on board by 4:30 P.M.
- The ship sails from Miami at 5:00 P.M.
- Allow 3 hours for traveling between the airport and the pier.

FEBRUARY: NONSTOP FLIGHTS FROM MINNEAPOLIS TO MIAMI			
Flight	Lv. Minneapolis	Arr. Miami	Meal
570	7:55 A.M. (CST)	12:20 P.M. (EST)	B
568	8:30 A.M. (CST)	12:55 P.M. (EST)	B
574	10:45 A.M. (CST)	3:10 P.M. (EST)	L
572	1:20 P.M. (CST)	5:45 P.M. (EST)	L

Notice the abbreviations CST and EST. CST stands for Central Standard Time and EST stands for Eastern Standard Time. These are two of the time zones in the United States. The Central Time Zone is one hour earlier than the Eastern Time Zone. For example, when the time in Miami is 10:00 A.M., the time in Minneapolis is 9:00 A.M.

Use the information above to answer the following questions:

21. What time must all the passengers be on board the ship? _____4:30 P.M._____

22. How much time is allowed for traveling from the Miami Airport to the pier in Miami? _____3 hours_____

23. What is the latest a plane can land so that the passengers will be able to get to the ship on time? _____1:30 P.M._____

24. Which flight would you recommend that Mr. and Mrs. Domingo take? _____Flight 568 or 570_____

25. Compute the flying time from Minneapolis (CST) to Miami (EST). _____3 hours 25 minutes_____

DETERMINING YOUR COMMISSION

A commission is an amount of money that you are paid for selling a cruise to a customer. The cruise line pays a travel agent a commission of 10% for each cruise.

Commission = Commission Rate × Total Sales

26. The price per person of the cruise is _____$1,580_____

27. Compute the commission that you will receive on the cruise you have booked for Mr. and Mrs. Domingo.

$316.00

COMPILING ITINERARY AND FLIGHT INFORMATION

The final step is to prepare an itinerary for the customer that shows all the travel plans and costs.

28. Refer to the cruise itinerary and the airline schedule to help you complete the itinerary below for Mr. and Mrs. Domingo.

FRIENDLY TRAVELERS, INC.					
Date _____			Itinerary for: _____ Mr. & Mrs. Domingo _____		
ITINERARY: 7-DAY CARIBBEAN CRUISE					
Date/Day	**From**	**To**	**Flight**	**Lv.**	**Arr.**
2/5–Sun	Minneapolis	Miami	568	8:30 A.M. (CST)	12:55 (EST)
2/5–Sun	Cruise begins from Miami			5:00 P.M.	
2/6–Mon	At Sea				
2/7–Tues	Arrive in Cozumel, Mexico, at 9:30 A.M. Leave at 5:30 P.M.				
2/8–Wed	Arrive in Grand Cayman Island at Noon. Leave at 6:00 P.M.				
2/9–Thurs	Arrive in Jamaica at 8:30 A.M. Leave at 4:00 P.M.				
2/10–Fri	Arrive in Haiti at 9:00 A.M. Leave at 5:00 P.M.				
2/11–Sat	At sea				
2/12–Sun	Arrive in Miami at 8:30 A.M.				
2/12–Sun	Miami	Minneapolis	571	2:00 P.M.	4:35 P.M.
Cost per person: _____ $1,580.00 _____			Total cost: _____ $3,160.00		

INSIDE INFORMATION

A travel agent should:

- have an outgoing personality
- feel comfortable meeting all types of people
- be a good salesperson

- have a good knowledge of geography
- be able to use a calculator and computer

Minimum Education: High-school graduate

Related Careers: Tour Guide, Rental Car Agent

Starting Salary: $16,400–$20,400 per year on straight salary

HOME ECONOMIST

Alissa Jackson is a home economist. She and her husband, Gary, have two children. Melanie is in the second grade, and Molly, who is two years old, stays at home with Alissa.

Here are some of the ways Alissa uses mathematics.

COMPARING PRICES

Alissa uses math to get the best value for her money. On a recent trip to the supermarket, Alissa bought breakfast cereal, laundry detergent, and two kinds of fruit.

Here are the prices of three brands of cereal.

Raisins Plus	$2.49 (20 oz. box)
Raisin Power	$2.09 (20 oz. box)
Raisin Riot	$2.29 (20 oz. box)

Assume Alissa has these coupons.

| Raisins **75¢ OFF** PLUS | Raisin **40¢ OFF** POWER | Raisin **65¢ OFF** RIOT |

Alissa wants to buy one box of cereal, using a coupon. How much will she pay for:

1. Raisins Plus ___$1.74___   2. Raisin Power ___$1.69___   3. Raisin Riot ___$1.64___

4. Which cereal costs the least with the coupon? ___Raisin Riot___

There are several brands of detergent to choose from. Alissa is looking for the brand and size with the lowest **unit price,** or cost per ounce. To find the unit price, divide the total cost by the number of ounces the container holds. Then round to the nearest cent.

Find the unit price of the following brands of detergent.

BRAND	64 OZ. BOTTLE	UNIT PRICE	96 OZ. BOTTLE	UNIT PRICE
5. Super Suds	$2.60	$0.04	$2.88	$0.03
6. Bubbles	$3.95	$0.06	$4.80	$0.05
7. Punch!	$3.20	$0.05	$3.95	$0.04

8. Which bottle and brand of laundry detergent has the lowest unit price? ___Super Suds 96 oz.___

9. Compare the unit prices of the 64-oz bottles to the unit prices of the 96-oz bottles. Which size has the lower unit price? <u>96 oz.</u>

10. Which bottle of detergent should Alissa buy? Why? <u>Answers will vary. Some students</u>

<u>may choose the brand with the lowest unit price.</u>

11. Should she always buy the larger size simply because it has a lower unit price? Why or why not?

<u>Answers will vary. Some students may suggest buying a smaller size because a larger</u>

<u>size isn't needed or because they prefer a particular brand.</u>

12. What reasons, other than unit price, might make someone buy a product? <u>Answers will vary.</u>

<u>Possible answers include brand loyalty, quality of the product, quantity needed.</u>

Alissa wants to buy apples and bananas.

> APPLES: 5 FOR $1.00 – 25¢ EACH
> BANANAS: 49¢ PER POUND

13. Alissa wants 24 apples to make applesauce. Should she buy 24 or 25 apples? Explain?

<u>Possible answer: 25 apples; because 24 apples and 25 apples both cost $5.00.</u>

14. Alissa needs four bananas to make a loaf of banana bread. If she makes three loaves, how many bananas will she need? <u>12</u>

15. If they weigh about 4 pounds, about how much will the bananas she needs cost? <u>$2.00</u>

USING FRACTIONS IN A RECIPE

Here is Alissa's recipe for banana bread.

Banana Bread

Ingredients

1 cup sugar	$\frac{1}{3}$ cup water	$\frac{1}{4}$ teaspoon baking powder
$\frac{1}{3}$ cup butter, softened	$1\frac{2}{3}$ cups all-purpose	$\frac{1}{2}$ teaspoon nutmeg
2 eggs	flour	$2\frac{1}{4}$ teaspoons vanilla
$1\frac{1}{2}$ cups mashed ripe bananas (about 4 medium bananas)	1 teaspoon baking soda $\frac{1}{2}$ teaspoon salt	$\frac{1}{2}$ teaspoon almond extract

Directions

Heat oven to 350°. Grease the bottom of a 9" x 5" x 3" loaf pan. Mix the sugar and butter in a $2\frac{1}{2}$-quart bowl. Stir in the eggs until blended. Add the bananas and water. Beat for 30 seconds. Stir in the remaining ingredients until just moistened. Pour the mixture into the pan. Bake about 55 minutes or until a toothpick inserted in the center comes out clean. Cool for 5 minutes. Loosen the sides of the pan and remove the loaf from the pan. Cool completely before slicing. Yield: 1 loaf (24 slices). 120 calories per slice.

16. How many loaves can be made from this recipe? <u>1</u>

17. How many slices are in one loaf? <u>24</u> three loaves? <u>72</u>

HOME ECONOMIST

Alissa is going to bake three loaves of banana bread for the PTA Bake Sale. Complete the following list of ingredients with the amounts she will need.

18. sugar _____3 cups_____   19. butter _____1 cup_____

20. eggs _____6 eggs_____   21. mashed ripe bananas _____$4\frac{1}{2}$ cups_____

22. water _____1 cup_____   23. all-purpose flour _____5 cups_____

24. baking soda _____3 teaspoons_____   25. salt _____$1\frac{1}{2}$ teaspoons_____

26. baking powder _____$\frac{3}{4}$ teaspoon_____   27. nutmeg _____$1\frac{1}{2}$ teaspoons_____

28. vanilla _____$6\frac{3}{4}$ teaspoons_____   29. almond extract _____$1\frac{1}{2}$ teaspoons_____

30. How long must each loaf bake? _____55 minutes_____

31. If you put in a loaf at 2:30 P.M., when will it be done? _____3:25 P.M._____

Timing is an important part of cooking. Alissa plans her cooking so that each dish is ready at the same time.

ITEM	COOKING TIME
Leg of lamb	$1\frac{1}{2}$ hours
Rice	20 minutes
Broccoli	5 minutes

You want to serve dinner at 6:00 P.M. What time should you start cooking the

32. leg of lamb? _____4:30 P.M._____   33. rice? _____5:40 P.M._____   34. broccoli? _____5:55 P.M._____

UNDERSTANDING PRESCRIPTION DOSAGES

When Melanie and Molly are sick, the doctor sometimes prescribes medicine. Alissa must make sure that the children take the right amount of medicine at the right time. This is the label from the bottle of medicine that Melanie had to take when she had a cold.

```
Rx 783-162                Date: 02/15/99
Melanie Jackson
Take 1 Teaspoon every four hours.
Not to exceed four doses a day.
Dr. Viola
```

35. How large is one dose of this medicine? _____1 teaspoon_____

Alissa gives Melanie her first dose at 9:00 A.M. At what time should she give her

36. the second dose? _____1:00 P.M._____ 37. the third dose? _____5:00 P.M._____ 38. the fourth dose? _____9:00 P.M._____

39. If Melanie actually took the medicine every four hours, she would be taking it 6 times a day. Why does the prescription say "Not to exceed four doses a day?" _____Sample answer:_____

    It is understood that Melanie is not to be awakened at night to take the medicine. _____

Alissa determines the family budget and is responsible for paying the bills on time. Here is an estimate of the family's monthly expenses.

Gary earns about $1800 per month after taxes.

MONTHLY EXPENSES—THE JACKSON FAMILY			
Mortgage	$600	Auto Insurance	$ 65
Groceries	$400	Home Insurance	$ 65
Telephone	$ 35	Entertainment	$100
Utilities	$ 55	Miscellaneous	$375

40. What is the total of the Jackson's monthly expenses? ___$1,695___

41. After the expenses are paid, about how much is left over from Gary's monthly income? ___$100___

42. If Alissa puts about $100 a month in a savings account, about how much will she have saved in one year? ___$1,200___

Alissa has set goals for the family's expenses. For example, she doesn't want to spend more than 10% of Gary's pay on insurance. Find out what percent of Gary's pay is currently spent on insurance.

43. Find the total monthly cost of both types of insurance. ___$130___

44. Find the percent of Gary's pay that goes for insurance.

$$\underset{\text{Gary's pay}}{\$1,800} \times n = \underset{\text{Monthly insurance costs}}{\$130}$$

$$n = \underset{\text{Insurance costs}}{\$130} \div \underset{\text{Gary's pay}}{\$1,800}$$

$$n \approx \underset{\text{decimal}}{0.07} = \underset{\text{percent}}{7}\% \qquad \approx \text{means } \textit{approximately equal to}$$

Complete the table below. Round to the nearest percent.

	Expense	% of Pay	Goal	Within Goal?
45.	Insurance	7%	10%	Yes
46.	Groceries	22%	20%	No
47.	Entertainment	6%	10%	Yes
48.	Telephone, Utilities	5%	5%	Yes

INSIDE INFORMATION

A home economist should:

- compute with whole numbers, decimals, fractions, and units of time
- meet and talk with teachers, repairmen, insurance agents, doctors, dentists, and pharmacists
- plan and manage the family's budget
- handle simple household repairs
- plan and prepare meals

Minimum Education: Cooking and Child Care courses helpful

Starting Salary: No salary per se. A portion of the working spouse's salary is used.

Related Careers: Child Care Worker, Private Household Worker

AUTO MECHANIC

Jim Lord is the senior mechanic at a service station. He makes estimates and writes up the bills for all repair work, and he sets retail prices on parts and supplies. (The **retail price** is the price that the customer pays.)

CALCULATING PERCENT MARKUPS

Complete the inventory list below. To calculate the retail price of each item, follow the steps in the example below.

Example: The service station buys a case of 12 quarts of Single G oil for $17.29. The markup at the station is 50%. What should the retail price be?

- Find the *Price Per Unit*.

  $17.29 ÷ 12 = $1.44
  price per   units per   price per
  case   case   unit

- Find the *Markup*. (The markup is the amount the station adds to the unit price to cover expenses and to make a profit.)

  $1.44 × 0.5 = $0.72
  price per   50%   amount of markup
  unit   markup   rounded to the next
                          greater cent

- Find the *Retail Price Per Unit*.

  $1.44 + $0.72 = $2.16
  price per   markup   retail price
  unit   per unit

Calculate the retail price of each item.

	Item	Price Per Case	Units Per Case	Price Per Unit	50% Markup	Retail Price Per Unit
	Single G Oil	$17.29	12	$1.44	$ .72	$2.16
1.	Brake Fluid, 12 oz.	$22.68	12	$1.89	$ .95	$2.84
2.	Power Steering Fluid, 1 qt.	$34.68	12	$2.89	$1.45	$4.34
3.	Cleaner, 16 oz.	$20.28	12	$1.69	$ .85	$2.54
4.	Antifreeze/Coolant, 1 gal.	$29.94	6	$4.99	$2.50	$7.49
5.	Spark Plugs	$ 7.92	8	$0.99	$ .50	$1.49
6.	Oil Filters	$15.48	12	$1.29	$ .64	$1.94
7.	Air Filters	$ 5.95	1	$5.95	$2.98	$8.93
8.	Fuel Filters	$ 3.99	1	$3.99	$1.99	$5.99
9.	Fan Belts	$ 6.99	1	$6.99	$3.49	$10.49
10.	Wiper Blades	$ 4.49	1	$4.49	$2.25	$6.74

11. Use the prices from the previous table to complete the Tires, Battery, Acc., Parts section of the Safety Car-Check Service below.

TIRES, BATTERY, ACC., PARTS

QUAN.		AMOUNT	
1	OIL FILTER	1	94
1	AIR FILTER	8	93
1	FUEL FILTER	5	99
4	SPARK PLUGS	5	96
	TOTAL PARTS	22	82

LABOR AND SERVICE WORK

LABOR- 2½ HRS		100	00
TOTAL LABOR		100	00

SAFETY INSPECTION

	OK	SEE COMMENT		OK	SEE COMMENT
BATTERY			WIPER/ WASHERS		✓
CABLES			MUFFLER		
RADIATOR		✓	TAIL PIPE		
RADIATOR CAP			TIRES		
RADIATOR HOSE			WHEEL BALANCE		
FAN BELT		✓	WHEEL ALIGN- MENT		
LIGHTS			PCV VALVE		
BRAKE FLUID			AIR FILTER		

COMMENTS

WIPERS — LEAVE STREAKS ON WINDSHIELD
RADIATOR — LOW ON COOLANT / ANTIFREEZE
FAN BELTS — SHOW CRACKS FROM WEAR / AGE

WORK DONE BY	CUSTOMER'S SIGNATURE
	X

SAFETY "CAR-CHECK" SERVICE

MAKE OF CAR PLUTO	NAME SAM TOMPKINS		
MODEL ROCKET	ADDRESS 444 CENTRAL ST.		
LICENSE NO. 467 UB8	CITY WATERTON	STATE PA	ZIP CODE 09743
MILEAGE 36742.5	DATE		TELEPHONE NO. 555-2453

QUAN.	CUSTOMER ORDER	AMOUNT	
	GASOLINE FILL TANK ☐		
	NO-NOX GOOD GOLF ☐ GOLFTANE ☐		
	LUBRICATION ✓	4	95
	MOTOR OIL CHANGE ✓ ADD ☐		
5 QTS	SINGLE G ✓ PRIDE MOTOR ☐	10	15
	TRANSMISSION ADD ☐ CHANGE ☐		
	DIFFERENTIAL ADD ☐ CHANGE ☐		
	CAR WASH ☐		
	OIL FILTER ✓ AIR FILTER ✓	PRICE IN T.B.A PARTS AND LABOR SECTIONS	
	PCV VALVE ✓ GAS FILTER ✓		
	TUNE-UP ✓ ☐		
	WHEEL BALANCE ☐ ☐		

A.M.	✓ P.M.

TOTAL ABOVE	15	10
TOTAL PARTS	22	82
TOTAL LABOR	100	00
PAY THIS AMOUNT ➡	137	92

Auto Mechanic

After Jim fills in the prices for parts and supplies, he can total the estimated bill. Then he presents it to the customer for approval.

12. Why do you think it is important for Jim and the customer to use an estimated bill before any work is done?

Answers may very. Possible answers include the importance of agreeing to an estimate

before work begins, and an estimate allows the customer to make sure he can afford the

repairs.

13. The service station charges $40 per hour for labor. Jim estimates that the job will take $2\frac{1}{2}$ hours. What will be the total charge for labor? Write the amount under the section labeled LABOR AND SERVICE WORK on the form.

$100

14. Add *Total Above, Total Parts,* and *Total Labor* on the form. Fill in the *Pay This Amount* space on the form.

15. Is the customer spending more money on parts or on labor? *labor*

16. After the work is completed, Jim fills out the *Safety Inspection* box. He checks three items and writes his comments below. If you were the customer, which items would you replace right away? Why?

Answers may vary. Possible answers include replacing the coolant in the radiator because

if the car overheats, the engine could be ruined; replacing the fan belt because if the fan

belt breaks, the car will overheat within minutes.

17. The customer asks Jim to replace the windshield wipers and two fan belts. Using the inventory list on page 69, figure the total cost.

$27.72

18. Jim has written on the service form that the car will be ready in the afternoon. As he begins work on the car that morning, he realizes that he doesn't have the fuel filter that he needs. He can't finish the job that day. What should he do? Why?

Answers may vary. One possible answer is to call the owner so that the owner can make

plans to lease or borrow a car. Another possible answer is to call other service stations to

locate another filter.

On Thursdays and Fridays, Jim reads the meters on all the gasoline tanks and pumps. He does this at the close of the business day to check the accuracy of the gasoline inventories. Complete the chart below.

TANKS

Date	Regular	Premium	Super Premium
March 9	2,279.6	3,374.5	4,925.3
March 10	− 1,955.8	− 1,922.0	− 4,146.1
Gallons sold	**19.** 323.8	**20.** 1,452.5	**21.** 779.2

PUMPS

Date	Pump #	Regular	Pump #	Premium	Pump #	Super Premium
March 9	1	01,814.8	3	087,521.7	5	34,367.5
	2	+ 202,792.7	4	+ 137,521.7	6	+ 08,871.0
Totals		**22.** 204,607.5		**23.** 225,043.4		**24.** 43,238.5
March 10	1	02,139.0	3	088,505.1	5	34,642.1
	2	+ 202,792.2	4	+ 137,990.8	6	+ 09,375.6
Totals		**25.** 204,931.2		**26.** 226,495.9		**27.** 44,017.7

Jim now has his readings from the gasoline tanks and pumps. Find out whether the readings match.

	Pumps 1 and 2	Pumps 3 and 4	Pumps 5 and 6
March 10 totals	204,931.2	226,495.9	44,017.7
28. March 9 totals	− 204,607.5	− 225,043.4	− 43,238.5
29. Total Sold	323.7	1,452.5	779.2

30. Does the total gasoline sold from the pumps match the gasoline readings from the tanks? ___Yes___

31. Which type of gasoline sold the most gallons? ___Premium___

32. What is the total number of gallons of all grades of gasoline sold? ___2,555.4___

INSIDE INFORMATION

An auto mechanic should:

- be organized
- be able to budget his/her time well
- be able to explain procedures clearly to customers
- enjoy doing several different tasks during the day

Minimum Education: High-school graduate
   Vocational training in auto mechanics
   or on-the-job experience

Starting Salary: $250–$333 per week

Related Careers: Repair Service Estimator, Bus Mechanic

DEPARTMENT STORE CLERK

Jessica Greene is a high school junior. As part of a Marketing Education class, she works as a clerk at Hastings Department Store. She earns $5.15 per hour and gets three credits per semester. In addition to helping customers, Jessica has to know how to make change, use a computerized cash register, and calculate discount prices.

MAKING CHANGE

For every sale, the cash register calculates the total price, including the amount of sales tax. For cash purchases, you enter the amount of cash the customer gives you, and the cash register calculates the amount of change. But, you are to give the customer the correct change using the smallest number of coins and bills possible. For example, if a customer gets $20.25 in change, you would never give 20 $1-bills and 25 pennies. A customer would much prefer to receive a $20-bill and a quarter.

Show the fewest number of coins and bills to make each amount of change.

	Change Due	$20	$10	$5	$1	25¢	10¢	5¢	1¢
	$3.86	–	–	–	3	3	1	–	1
1.	8¢							1	3
2.	17¢						1	1	2
3.	54¢					2			4
4.	93¢					3	1	1	3
5.	$1.12				1		1		2
6.	$4.45				4	1	2		
7.	$8.37			1	3	1	1		2
8.	$13.24		1		3		2		4
9.	$27.80	1		1	2	3		1	
10.	$58.68	2	1	1	3	2	1	1	3

CONDUCTING A TRANSACTION

Computerized cash registers have made a clerk's work easier. Every clerk has an employee number which must be entered into the cash register when it is first turned on. Usually, the store assigns a number, but today you can choose your employee number. Select any four digits to form your employee number.

Employee number: ____ ____ ____ ____

USING RATIO, PROPORTION, AND PERCENT

73

A. Whenever you use a cash register, the first piece of information you enter will be your employee number. Next you enter the code number for the type of sale. Use the table below.

SALES CODES			
Type of Sale	**Code**	**Type of Sale**	**Code**
Cash	01	Return	02

B. A scanner is used to scan the bar code tag on each item of merchandise. This automatically enters the price and any department information. If more than one of an item is purchased, the appropriate key is also entered. For example, if a customer is buying 2 of the same kind of shirt, you would enter 2 after scanning the bar code tag on one of the shirts. The cash register does the computation.

C. The code for the type of payment is entered next. The codes are shown below.

PAYMENT CODES			
Type of Payment	**Code**	**Type of Payment**	**Code**
Cash/Check	01	Charge	02

D. If the customer is paying by Cash/Check, the amount given to you by the customer is entered. For instance, if the sales total comes to $38.16, the customer might give you $40.00. This is the amount entered in the cash register. The register computes the change due. If the customer is paying by check, the amount of the check, which would be the same as the total sale, is entered.

E. If the customer is charging the amount due on a credit card, a special input device is used to "read" the credit card number. The credit card is "swiped" across the device which then automatically inputs the credit card number and charges the customer's credit card account.

Enter each sale into the cash register. Follow the steps below. Refer to the tables above for the Sales Codes and Payment Codes.

STEPS FOR USING THE CASH REGISTER

Step 1. Enter your employee number.
Step 2. Enter the sale code.
Step 3. Scan the merchandise and key in quantity if necessary.
Step 4. Determine the total amount of the sale.
Step 5. Enter the payment code.
Step 6. Enter the amount of cash received by the customer. If a credit card is used, "swipe" the credit card to enter the transaction.
Step 7. Give the customer any change due and the receipt for the transaction.

Situation: A customer buys a coffeemaker.
Type of Sale: Sale
Type of Payment: Charge
Price: $45.00

11. Employee number: ____ ____ ____ ____

12. Sale Code: _0_ _1_

13. Price per item: ____$45.00____

14. Quantity: ____1____

15. Total Sale: ____$45.00____

16. Payment Code: _0_ _3_

17. Amount received/Change: ____$45.00____

DEPARTMENT STORE CLERK

Situation: A customer buys a hair dryer.
Type of Sale: Sale
Type of Payment: Cash
Price: $25.64
Amount Received: $30.00

18. Employee number: ____ ____ ____ ____

19. Sale code: _0_ _1_

20. Price per item: _____$25.64_____

21. Quantity: _____1_____

22. Total Sale: _____$25.64_____

23. Payment Code: _0_ _1_

24. Amount received/Change: ___$30.00/$4.36___

Situation: A customer buys 3 men's polo shirts.
Type of Sale: Sale
Type of Payment: Charge
Price: $36.00

25. Employee number: ____ ____ ____ ____

26. Sale code: _0_ _1_

27. Price per item: _____$36.00_____

28. Quantity: _____3_____

29. Total Sale: _____$108.00_____

30. Payment Code: _0_ _3_

31. Amount received/Change: _____$108.00_____

CALCULATING EMPLOYEE DISCOUNTS USING PERCENTAGES

One of the advantages of being an employee at a department store is that you get a discount on everything you buy at the store. At Hastings, each clerk is entitled to a 20% discount.

Example: Mother's Day is two weeks away. Your family wants to surprise your mother with a microwave oven. The regular price is $200.00. However, it is on sale for 30% off. How much will you pay for the microwave oven with the sale price and your employee discount?

Step 1:   Find the sale price.

$200	×	0.30	=	$60.00
orig. price		% of sale		amount saved
$200	−	$60.00	=	$140.00
orig. price		amount saved		SALE PRICE

Step 2:   Apply the employee discount.

$140	×	0.20	=	$28.00
sale price		% of employee discount		amount saved
$140	−	$28.00	=	$112.00
sale price		amount saved		EMPLOYEE PRICE

You can buy the microwave oven for $112.00, plus tax.

Calculate the discounted price you will pay for each item. Remember that the employee discount is 20%. When computing the discount, write 20% as 0.20.

32. Item: Dress   Original price: $85.00   Sale: 25% off

$\underline{\ \ 85\ \ }$ × $\underline{\ \ 0.25\ \ }$ = $\underline{\ \ 21.25\ \ }$
orig. price   % of sale   amount saved

$\underline{\ \ 85\ \ }$ − $\underline{\ \ 21.25\ \ }$ = $\underline{\ \ 63.75\ \ }$
orig. price   amount saved   SALE PRICE

$\underline{\ \ 63.75\ \ }$ × $\underline{\ \ 0.20\ \ }$ = $\underline{\ \ 12.75\ \ }$
sale price   % of employee discount   amount saved

$\underline{\ \ 63.75\ \ }$ − $\underline{\ \ 12.75\ \ }$ = $\underline{\ \ 51.00\ \ }$
sale price   amount saved   EMPLOYEE PRICE

33. Item: Sweater   Original price: $60.00

Employee price: $ 48.00   Amount saved: $ 12.00

34. Item: Sunglasses   Original price: $32.00

Employee price $ 25.60   Amount saved: $ 6.40

35. Item: Comforter   Original price: $215.00   Sale: 50% off

Employee price: $ 86.00   Total saved: $ 129.00

36. Item: Sneakers   Original price: $38.00   Sale: 25% off

Employee price: $ 22.80   Total saved: $ 15.20

---

*I*NSIDE *I*NFORMATION

A department store clerk should:

- enjoy working with people
- have good math skills
- be able to work efficiently
- be able to address customer demands patiently and courteously

Minimum Education: High-school graduate (full time)
   High-school in progress (part time)

Starting Salary: $5.15 per hour

Related Careers: Cashier, Rental Clerk

GRAPHIC DESIGNER

Anil Masouf is a freelance graphic designer living in New York City. He works out of a small studio located in the Upper West Side of Manhattan. Anil works primarily for publishing firms illustrating children's books but he also creates other designs which he sells to small advertising firms.

Some days Anil works only a few hours, while on other days he begins work before dawn and does not finish until after it is dark. He enjoys working different hours and the challenge of creating different designs for different projects.

FINDING UNKNOWN DIMENSIONS OF SIMILAR FIGURES

When he is working on book illustrations, Anil must not only create satisfactory designs, but he also must make sure the size of the design meets the page specifications. Usually a design needs to fit a designated area on a page of written material. A publisher will assign Anil several illustrations, each of which is to fit in a specific section on a page.

Below are some examples of the spaces designated for Anil's illustrations. Each page is a rectangle measuring $8\frac{1}{2}$ by 11 inches. To allow for margins, the measurements 8×10 inches are used. Illustrations are also rectangles but are smaller. Each of the pages shown below has space designated for one or two illustrations. Anil must know the width and the length of each illustration but only one of these dimensions is given. Since the page and the illustrations are similar figures, the unknown dimensions can be determined by setting up and solving a proportion.

Determine the unknown dimension for the illustrations Anil must draw.

$$\frac{8 \text{ in.}}{10 \text{ in.}} = \frac{4 \text{ in.}}{?}$$

$$8 \times ? = 10 \times 4$$

$$\frac{(8 \times ?)}{8} = \frac{40}{8}$$

$? = 5$ inches   **Length of illustration: 5 inches**

1. Length of illustration: _____ 5 inches _____

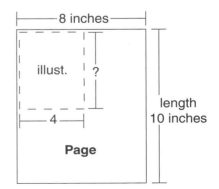

2. Width of illustration: _____ 6.4 inches _____

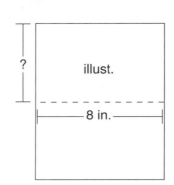

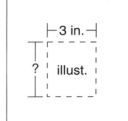

3. Length of illustration: _____ 3.75 inches _____

4. Length of each illustration: _____ 2.5 inches _____

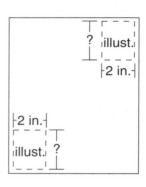

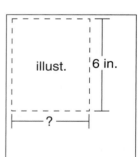

5. Width of illustration: _____ 4.8 inches _____

Determine the unknown side for each of the following pairs of similar rectangles.

6. Rectangle A: $w = 6$ in.; $l = 9$ in.
Rectangle B: $w = $ _____ 10 in. _____ ; $l = 15$ in.

7. Rectangle A: $w = $ _____ 5 in. _____ ; $l = 11$ in.
Rectangle B: $w = 2\frac{1}{2}$ in.; $l = 5\frac{1}{2}$ in.

8. Rectangle A: $w = 9$ cm; $l = $ _____ 27.6 cm _____
Rectangle B: $w = 7$ cm; $l = 21.5$ cm

9. Rectangle A: $w = 12.4$ cm; $l = 16.2$ cm
Rectangle B: $w = $ _____ 4.59 cm _____ ; $l = 6$ cm

10. Rectangle A: $w = 22\frac{2}{3}$ in.; $l = 31\frac{1}{4}$ in.
Rectangle B: $w = 14\frac{1}{2}$ in.; $l = $ _____ 20 in. _____

GRAPHIC DESIGNER

WRITING PERCENTS AS DECIMALS

Frequently, Anil is asked to reduce or enlarge an existing design to fit a client's needs. He does this by multiplying the width and the length of the design by the desired percentage of reduction or enlargement. Calculate the new dimensions of the following design widths and lengths based on the client's specifications.

Old Dimensions: w = 4 inches; l = 6 inches
Specification: Reduce by 25%
New Dimensions: w = .25 × 4 = 1.0 inch; 4 inches − 1 inch = 3 inches
l = .25 × 6 = 1.5 inches; 6 inches − 1.5 inches = **4.5 inches**

11. Old Dimensions: $w = 3\frac{1}{2}$ inches; l = 5 inches

Specification: Reduce by 50%

New Dimensions: w = _____ $1\frac{3}{4}$ inches _____

l = _____ $2\frac{1}{2}$ inches _____

12. Old Dimensions: $w = 11\frac{1}{2}$ inches; l = 14 inches

Specification: Reduce by 30%

New Dimensions: w = _____ 8 inches _____

l = _____ $9\frac{4}{5}$ inches _____

13. Old Dimensions: $w = 2\frac{1}{2}$ inches; $l = 3\frac{1}{2}$ inches

Specification: Enlarge by 50%

New Dimensions: w = _____ $3\frac{3}{4}$ inches _____

l = _____ $5\frac{1}{4}$ inches _____

14. Old Dimensions: w = 5 inches; l = 7 inches

Specification: Reduce by 25%

New Dimensions: w = _____ $3\frac{3}{4}$ inches _____

l = _____ $5\frac{1}{4}$ inches _____

15. Old Dimensions: w = 10 inches; l = 12 inches

Specification: Reduce by 30%

New Dimensions: w = _____ 7 inches _____

l = _____ $8\frac{2}{5}$ inches _____

Convert the following fractions or percentages to a decimal.

16. 17.3%   _____ .173 _____

17. 8%   _____ .08 _____

18. $\frac{4}{5}$ _____ .80 _____

19. 66.5%   _____ .665 _____

20. $\frac{10}{20}$ _____.50_____

21. $\frac{3}{8}$ _____.375_____

Convert the following fractions into decimals, then into percentages.

22. $\frac{3}{4}$ _____.75; 75%_____

23. $\frac{1}{4}$ _____.25; 25%_____

24. $\frac{2}{3}$ _____.6667; 67%_____

25. $\frac{1}{2}$ _____.50; 50%_____

Read through each situation. Provide the answer in the space provided.

26. A publisher would like Anil to illustrate a 36-page children's book. The publisher would like approximately $\frac{3}{4}$ of the book to be illustrated. About how many pages will be illustrated?

_____About 27 pages will be illustrated._____

27. A collection of fairy tales that Anil illustrated several years ago is being revised. The new edition will have larger illustrations. Half of the illustrations will be enlarged by 25%, and the other half will be enlarged by 40%. All of the old illustrations measured four inches by four inches. What will the new dimensions be in the revised edition?

_____Half of the illustrations will measure five inches by five inches; the other half will measure_____

_____$5\frac{3}{5}$ inches by $5\frac{3}{5}$ inches._____

INSIDE INFORMATION

A graphic designer should:

- have strong artistic ability
- be able to communicate ideas through artistic media
- be able to present an impressive portfolio to clients
- be extremely self-motivated and self-confident

Minimum Education: Although formal training requirements do not exist, a college degree is strongly recommended.

Starting Salary: $23,000–$27,000 per year

Related Careers: Landscape Architect, Interior Decorator, Photographer

AUTOMOBILE SALESPERSON

Steve Morales is a salesperson at an automobile dealer's showroom. He shows the newest models of cars to customers and gives them the information they need to make a decision.

DETERMINING COSTS

Pretend that you are a salesperson at an automobile dealer. You have just met Mr. and Mrs. Harris, who want to buy a new car. They would like to spend about $15,000. The first step is to ask Mr. and Mrs. Harris some basic questions about the car they currently own and which features they would like in their new car. Their answers are shown on the Customer Information Form below.

CUSTOMER INFORMATION FORM

Name *Mr. & Mrs. Ronald Harris*   Date _____

Address *980 Apple Hill Rd.*   Home Tel. *978-6531*

Occupation *Electrician, Accountant*   Work Tel. *401-0708*

Model Interested In *Tri Star*   New *✓*   Used _____

Present Car *Rocket*   Year *1993*

Referred By *Newspaper ad & television ads*

Family Size *2 adults, 3 children*   Number of Drivers *2*

Equipment Desired *4-door sedan*

EXTRA FEATURES

Air conditioning	$800	AM/FM Radio, CD Player	$670
Automatic transmission	$300	Sun roof	$740
Special wheel covering	$500	Leather seats	$895
Remote keyless entry	$190	Deluxe instrument panel	$200

Mr. and Mrs. Harris would like to buy a silver, 4-door sedan that has a list price of $12,948.

1. Mr. and Mrs. Harris decide that they can afford $2500 for extra features over the $12,948 list price. Which extra features would you recommend to the Harrises? Remember that the cost of the extra features cannot be more than $2,500.

   Answers will vary. _____

2. The Harrises will need to pay a $500 destination charge and $715 in sales tax. If they order no extra features, what will be the total purchase price of the car?

   $14,163.00 _____

CALCULATING DOWN PAYMENTS AND MONTHLY PAYMENTS

The next step is to discuss how Mr. and Mrs. Harris will **finance,** or pay for, the car. You point out that they will have to make a down payment on the car. A **down payment** is a certain percentage of the total price of the car that the customer pays when buying a car. The Harrises will be getting a bank loan to help pay for the car. The amount of the required down payment depends on the bank.

For example, First Federal Bank requires a down payment of 30% on a car that costs $14,163. To find the amount of the down payment, find 30% of $14,163.

$$30\% \text{ of } \$14,163 = 0.30 \times \$14,163 = \$4,248.90$$

A 30% down payment would be $ 4,248.90.

You mention three banks that offer three different payment plans. Calculate the amount of the down payment for a $14,163 car at each bank.

	Bank	Required Down Payment	Amount of Down Payment
3.	First State Bank	25%	$3,540.75
4.	National Savings Bank	20%	$2,832.60
5.	Citywide Bank	15%	$2,124.45

At first glance, it looks as if Citywide Bank offers the best deal because its down payment is the lowest. However, it's not that simple. Sometimes, the lower the down payment, the higher the interest rate. The **interest rate** is the percentage of the borrowed money which the bank charges for the loan. In order to make the sale, you need to show the Harrises what their monthly payment might be.

To calculate the monthly payment, first calculate how much the Harrises will owe after the down payment has been made. To do this, subtract the amount of the down payment from the price of the car.

How much will Mr. and Mrs. Harris owe on the car after they pay the down payment at

6. First State Bank? $10,622.25 **7.** National Savings Bank? $11,330.40 **8.** Citywide Bank? $12,038.55

Most banks offer three different payment plans. The Harrises could pay off the car over two years, three years, or four years. Automobile salespeople use computer software programs to find the monthly payment for a loan. The table below shows the monthly payments for each of the payment plans.

$8\frac{1}{2}\%$	Monthly Payment		
Loan Amount	2 Year	3 Year	4 Year
$10,000	454.55	315.67	246.48
$11,000	500.01	347.24	271.13
$12,000	545.46	378.81	295.77
$13,000	590.92	410.37	320.42

Name _____ Class _____ Date _____

AUTOMOBILE SALESPERSON

Example: Find the monthly payment
for a $10,000 loan at an
interest rate of 8.5% that is
paid back over three years.

- Find $10,000 in the column
  titled LOAN AMOUNT.
- Move right to the column titled
  3 YEARS
- The monthly payment is
  $315.67.

First State Bank and Citywide Bank
offer interest rates of 9.5%. Mr. and
Mrs. Harris decide to apply for a
$12,000 loan from the National
Savings Bank because it offers an
interest rate of 8.5%.

Use the monthly payment table to find the monthly payment if Mr. and Mrs. Harris repay the loan over:

9. 2 years ____$545.46____   **10.** 3 years ____$378.81____   **11.** 4 years ____$295.77____

CALCULATING TOTAL INTEREST TO BE PAID

To calculate the total amount you have to pay back, multiply the monthly payment by the number of
months to pay off the loan.

Example: A 4-year loan of $13,000 at an interest rate of 8.5% has a monthly payment of $320.42. Find the
total amount of the loan.

There are 48 months in 4 years.

$320.42	×	48	=	$15,380.16
monthly payment		months		total amount to be paid back

To calculate the amount of interest paid, subtract the amount borrowed from the total amount to be paid
back.

Example: $15,380.16 − $13,000 = $2,380.16
total amount   amount   interest
to be paid back   borrowed   charged

Complete the table to calculate the total amount to be paid back and the amount of interest charged on
each of the payment plans for Mr. and Mrs. Harris's $12,000 loan.

	Type of Loan	Months to Pay Back Loan	Monthly Payment	Total Amount to Be Paid Back	Interest Charged
12.	2 year	24	$545.46	$13,091.04	$1,091.04
13.	3 year	36	$378.81	$13,637.16	$1,637.16
14.	4 year	48	$295.77	$14,196.96	$2,196.96

Notice that the sooner the Harrises pay off the loan, the less interest they have to pay.

How much less interest do the Harrises have to pay if they pay back the loan in

15. 2 years instead of 3 years? _____$546.12_____ **16.** 2 years instead of 4 years? _____$1,105.92_____

17. 3 years instead of 4 years? _____$559.80_____

18. The Harrises ask your opinion of which payment plan is the best. What would you recommend?

_____**Answers will vary. If the Harrises can afford the higher monthly payment, it might be better**_____

_____**to pay the loan in 2 years.**_____

FIGURING A SALES COMMISSION

Let's assume that the bank approves the Harrises' loan and they drive away with their dream car. Now it's time to compute the commission on your sale. A **commission** is a percent of the selling price that you earn by selling the car. You sold the car for $14,163. The cost of the car to the dealer was $13,463.

Find the difference between the selling price and the cost to the dealer.

$14,163 − $13,463 = $700

From this $700, subtract a $300 "pack," or the amount that goes to the dealer to cover the expense of having the car in the showroom.

$700 − $300 = $400

Your commission is cased on the $400. You earn a commission of 25%.

$400 × 0.25 = $100

Your commission on the sale is $100.

Calculate your commission on each of the following sales.

	Sale Price	−	Cost to Dealer	−	Pack ⟶	Comm. Base	×	% of Comm.	=	Comm. Earned
19.	$15,000		$14,200		$300	$500		0.25		$125
20.	$17,000		$16,100		$300	$600		0.25		$150
21.	$25,000		$23,900		$300	$800		0.25		$200
22.	$32,000		$24,000		$300	$7,700		0.25		$1,925
23.	$41,700		$32,500		$300	$8,900		0.25		$2,225

INSIDE INFORMATION

A automobile salesperson should:

- be able to compute with whole numbers, decimals, and percents
- be friendly and outgoing
- enjoy selling
- know when to be persistent and when not to be persistent
- be able to take disappointments in stride

Minimum Education: High-school graduate   *Starting salary:* $15,000–$30,000 per year including commissions

Related Careers: Real Estate Agent, Sales Representative

UNIT 3

Using Formulas, Measurement, and Geometry

UNIT 3

Using Formulas, Measurement, and Geometry

COMPUTER PROGRAMMER

Justine Larson is a computer programmer for a software company in California. She spends most of her workday updating and repairing specific programs, or instructions, that computers use in order to function. Justine receives assignments from the software engineers that detail how she is to update, repair, modify, or expand an existing program.

Each step of a computer program is broken down into a logical series of instructions that the computer can follow. Justine codes the steps in one of many computer languages— FORTRAN, C, Pascal, Java, C++, Visual Basic, or Ada are some examples. This means she must be familiar with the code notations specific to each language.

USING PASCAL TO WRITE A SIMPLE HELLO PROGRAM

Every computer language has a strict set of rules that a programmer must follow. The code that a programmer writes must incorporate these rules, or the computer will not understand them. A simple set of instructions that demonstrates the rules of a particular computer language is a **Hello Program.** This is a short program that produces a written message (usually the greeting "Hello" or something similar) on the monitor. An example Hello Program written in the computer language called Pascal is shown below.

Sample Hello Program (Pascal):

Line A   program HELLO (output);
Line B   begin
Line C   writeln('Hello. How are you?')
Line D   end.

In Pascal, the first line of the program, **Line A**, defines the procedure. In this case, the procedure is HELLO. The next line, **Line B,** begins the procedure named in the previous line. **Line C** contains the instructions to be carried out by the program. In this example, the instruction is to display the phrase, "Hello. How are you?" In Pascal, phrases that are to be displayed as text are written inside single quotes. Notice also that when using Pascal, this writeln line must be indented. Finally, the last line, **Line D,** defines the end of the procedure.

In **Lines A–D,** the coded parts of the program are the notations: *program HELLO (output); begin; writeln; and end.*

In **Lines A–D** the only part of the program that is displayed is the phrase, "Hello. How are you?" as defined on **Line C.**

Practice writing your own Hello Program lines in the exercises below.

1. Rewrite Line C so that the Hello Program displays the statement, "How are you doing today?"

   writeln('How are you doing today?') (Answer should be indented.)

Using the same Pascal format, write a four-line Hello Program that displays the statement, "Are you going to be home this weekend?"

2. Line A: programWEEKEND(output);

3. Line B: begin

4. Line C: writeln('Are you going to be home this weekend?')

5. Line D: end.

CREATING AN IF-THEN LOOP PROGRAM IN VISUAL BASIC

If-then loops are a method by which a program can make decisions based on either existing conditions, or on user input. A **Hello Loop Program** written in a computer language called Visual Basic is shown below.

Sample Hello Loop Program (Visual Basic):

Line A   If text1.text = **"Hello there."** then
Line B   Let text1.text = **"Hello to you too!"**
Line C   End if

In **Lines A–C,** the coded part of this program are the notations: *If text1.text = then; Let text1.text =; and End if.*

In **Lines A–C,** the values enclosed within quotes, **"Hello there."** and **"Hello to you too!"** are the parts of the program that are displayed on the monitor. Notice that in Visual Basic, items to be displayed are enclosed within double quotations.

The information displayed on the monitor would look something like this:

> **Hello there.**
> **Hello to you too!**

In the following exercises, write your own instructions for a Hello Loop Program in Visual Basic.

6. Rewrite Line A of the Loop Program in Visual Basic so that it instructs the computer to look for the statement, "How are you today?"

   If text1.text = "How are you today?" then

7. Rewrite Line B so that it instructs the computer to respond with the statement "Good Morning!"

   Let text1.text = "Good Morning!"

COMPUTER PROGRAMMER

Write a Loop Program in Visual Basic that instructs the computer to reply to the question, "Are you feeling well today?" with the response, "Very well thank you."

8. Line A: _If text1.text = "Are you feeling well today?" then_

9. Line B: _Let text1.text = "Very well thank you."_

10. Line C: _End if_

USING A COMPUTER PROGRAM TO SOLVE A FORMULA

Many computer programs are used to solve mathematical formulas. Writing a program to solve a basic formula is simple. The language called C++ is used below to write a program that determines the area of a rectangle using the formula: area = $l \times w$.

Line A: double length, width, area;
Line B: cout<< "Please enter length/n";
Line C: cin>> length;
Line D: cout<< "Please enter width/n";
Line E: cin>> width;
Line F: area = l * w ;
Line G: cout<< "The area is equal to" << area "." ;

As was the case in the previous examples, phrases that are to be displayed on the screen are enclosed within quotation marks. (Pascal used the single quotation mark.) In the example above, **Line A** defines the variables to be used—length, width, and area. (The word "double" is a C++ code notation.) In **Line B,** the output (cout) statement—"Please enter width"—is defined. (The "/n" is a C++ code notation.) **Line C** instructs the computer to wait for the user to input (cin) a value for length. **Lines D** and **E** repeat the same thing as Lines B and C using width instead of length. **Line F** instructs the computer to use the formula, area = l * w, with the inputted values for length and width (Note that the asterisk is used to denote multiplication.). **Line G** displays the answer in the output statement "The area is equal to" ___.

Using the example above as a reference, write a program in C++ to determine the perimeter of a rectangle.

Formula: Perimeter = 2(length) + 2(width)

11. Line A: _double length, width, perimeter;_

12. Line B: _cout<< "Please enter length/n";_

13. Line C: _cin>> length;_

14. Line D: _cout<< "Please enter width/n";_

15. Line E: _cin>> width;_

16. Line F: _area = (2 * length) + (2 * width);_

17. Line G: _cout<< "The perimeter is equal to" << perimeter".";_

18. What notation is used to mark the end of each line? _the semicolon_

19. What is another way that the formula in Line F could be written? _area = l + l + w + w;_

20. Describe what the monitor will display as a result of this program.

Please enter length
_____

(length is inputted by user)
_____

Please enter width
_____

(width is inputted by user)
_____

The perimeter is equal to (value determined by the computer.)
_____

Use the same format as above to write a program which determines the area of a triangle. (Formula: Area = $\frac{1}{2}$(base × height)

21. Line A: ___ double base, height, area;

22. Line B: ___ cout<< "Please enter base/n";

23. Line C: ___ cin>> base;

24. Line D: ___ cout<< "Please enter height/n";

25. Line E: ___ cin>> height;

26. Line F: ___ area = (base * height)/2;

27. Line G: ___ cout<< "The area is equal to" << area".";

INSIDE INFORMATION

A computer programmer should:

- be detail-oriented
- be patient and persistent
- be able to work with abstract concepts
- be comfortable working under close supervision

Minimum Education: College education   *Starting Salary:* $32,500–$39,000

Related Careers: Computer Scientist, Financial Analyst

FIREFIGHTER

"There is much more to firefighting than just putting the wet stuff on the red stuff," says Terry Reese, a firefighter from Michigan. If you think that firefighters simply attach a hose to a hydrant and start pumping, you're in for a big surprise. Mathematics plays an important part in fighting every fire.

Firefighters rely on formulas to determine the engine pressure necessary for supplying the nozzles with the correct volume and pressure of water. In this lesson, you will study some of the most important formulas that firefighters use. You may want to use a calculator throughout this lesson.

COMPUTING FRICTION LOSS

One key to putting out a fire is proper **nozzle pressure.** Water must be flowing fast enough and strong enough to form a stream that will reach the fire. Proper nozzle pressure is also an important safety factor. Too much pressure makes the hose difficult to hold. Not enough pressure may cause the firefighter to get burned.

The nozzle pressure is controlled by the Fire Engine Operator, who is in charge of the water flowing in and out of the fire engine. If he raises engine pressure, nozzle pressure increases. If he lowers engine pressure, nozzle pressure decreases.

In order to find out what engine pressure is needed, you have to estimate the **friction loss.** Friction is created as water flowing through the fire hose comes in contact with the hose lining. As water flows through hydrants, hoses, and nozzles, it loses pressure. The friction loss is the pressure that is lost. Following are some of the factors that affect friction loss:

- The narrower the hose, the greater the friction.
- The faster that water flows, the greater the friction.
- The farther that water has to travel, the greater the friction.

Therefore, the first step in determining the correct engine pressure is to estimate the friction loss that will occur. In operating a pump at a fire, with a standard hose of a diameter of $2\frac{1}{2}$ inches, firefighters can use the following formula:

$$FL = 2Q^2 + Q$$

In this formula, FL stands for friction loss per 100 feet, and Q stands for the gallons per minute divided by 100. This is the one formula that should be memorized by every pump operator because it can be used while standing in the street.

Example: Estimate the friction loss for a flow of 300 gallons per minute (gpm) through 400 feet of $2\frac{1}{2}$-inch hose.

Step 1: Find Q.

$Q = 300$ gpm $\div 100$
$Q = 3$

Step 2: Calculate the friction loss for 100 feet of hose. Substitute the value of Q into the formula.

$FL = 2Q^2 + Q$
$FL = (2 \times 3 \times 3) + 3$
$FL = 18 + 3$
$FL = 21$ pounds per square inch (psi)

Step 3: Calculate the total friction loss.

In this example, the hose is 400 feet long. Since the friction loss for 100 feet of hose is 21 psi, multiply 4×21 to find the total friction loss for 400 feet of hose.

4×21 psi $= 84$ psi

The total friction loss is about 84 psi.

1. Estimate the friction loss for a flow of 200 gallons per minute (gpm) through 400 feet of $2\frac{1}{2}$-inch hose.

Step 1: Find Q.

$Q = \underline{\textbf{200}}$ gpm $\div$ 100

$Q = \underline{\textbf{2}}$

Step 2: Calculate the friction loss for 100 feet of hose. Substitute the value of Q into the formula.

$FL = 2Q^2 + Q$

$FL = (\underline{\textbf{2}} \times \underline{\textbf{2}} \times \underline{\textbf{2}}) + \underline{\textbf{2}}$

$FL = \underline{\textbf{8}} + \underline{\textbf{2}}$

$FL = \underline{\textbf{10}}$ pounds per square inch (psi)

Step 3: Calculate the total friction loss.

$\underline{\textbf{400}} \div 100$ ft $= \underline{\textbf{4}}$
Length of hose   Factor for hose length

$\underline{\textbf{4}} \times \underline{\textbf{10}} = \underline{\textbf{40}}$ psi
Factor for   Friction loss   Total friction
hose length   per 100 feet   loss

FIREFIGHTER

Estimate the total friction loss in pounds per square inch (psi) in a $2\frac{1}{2}$-inch hose for each of the following situations.

	Flow in gpm	Q	Fl per 100 feet $FL = 2Q^2 + Q$	Length of hose (in feet)	Total Friction Loss
2.	600	6	78 psi	400 ft	312 psi
3.	300	3	21 psi	700 ft	147 psi
4.	800	8	136 psi	500 ft	680 psi
5.	500	5	55 psi	350 ft	192.5 psi

COMPUTING THE ENGINE PRESSURE

Remember that the force of the water coming out of the nozzle is affected by the engine pressure. The greater the engine pressure, the greater the pressure of the water flowing from the nozzle.

The engine pressure depends on the nozzle pressure and friction loss. Now that you know how to calculate the friction loss, you can compute what the engine pressure should be.

ENGINE PRESSURE = NOZZLE PRESSURE + TOTAL FRICTION LOSS

$$EP = NP + TFL$$

Example: The nozzle pressure should be 100 pounds per square inch (psi). Compute the engine pressure needed when the total friction loss is 45 psi.

$EP = NP + TFL$
$EP = 100 + 45$
$EP = 145$ psi

The firefighter in charge of the gauges would set the gauge for the engine pressure at 145 psi.

Calculate the engine pressure that is needed in each situation.

	Nozzle Pressure	Total Friction Loss	Engine Pressure
6.	100 psi	75 psi	175 psi
7.	50 psi	24 psi	74 psi
8.	75 psi	41 psi	116 psi
9.	80 psi	67 psi	147 psi
10.	65 psi	58 psi	123 psi

Often a firefighter has to find the total friction loss in order to determine the necessary engine pressure.

Example: You arrive at the scene of a fire. You are in charge of monitoring the gauges and setting the engine pressure. A 600-foot line of $2\frac{1}{2}$-inch hose supplies 300 gpm. The nozzle pressure should be 100 psi. What should the engine pressure be?

Step 1: Find the total friction loss

$$FL = 2Q^2 + Q$$
$$FL = (2 \times 3 \times 3) + 3$$
$$FL = 18 + 3$$
$$FL = 21 \text{ psi per 100 ft}$$
$$TFL = 6 \times 21$$
$$TFL = 126 \text{ psi}$$

Step 2: Find the engine pressure.

$$EP = NP + TFL$$
$$EP = 100 + 126$$
$$EP = 226 \text{ psi}$$

You should set the gauge for the engine pressure at 226 psi to deliver enough water to put out the fire.

11. A 500-ft line of $2\frac{1}{2}$-inch hose will supply 200 gpm. The nozzle pressure should be 100 psi. What should the engine pressure be?

Step 1: Find the total friction loss.

$$FL = 2Q^2 + Q$$
$$FL = (\underline{\ \ 2\ \ } \times \underline{\ \ 2\ \ } \times \underline{\ \ 2\ \ }) + \underline{\ \ 2\ \ }$$
$$FL = \underline{\ \ 8\ \ } + \underline{\ \ 2\ \ }$$
$$FL = \underline{\ \ 10\ \ } \text{ psi per 100 ft}$$
$$TFL = \underline{\ \ 10\ \ } \times \underline{\ \ 5\ \ }$$
$$TFL = \underline{\ \ 50\ \ } \text{ psi}$$

Step 2: Find the engine pressure.

$$EP = NP + TFL$$
$$EP = \underline{\ \ 100\ \ } + \underline{\ \ 50\ \ }$$
$$EP = \underline{\ \ 150\ \ } \text{ psi}$$

12. A $2\frac{1}{2}$-inch hose that is 800 feet long will supply 150 gpm. The nozzle pressure should be 80 psi. Calculate the engine pressure. _____ 128 psi

13. A 700-foot line of $2\frac{1}{2}$-inch hose will supply 250 gpm. The nozzle pressure should be 50 psi. What should the engine pressure be? _____ 155 psi

INSIDE INFORMATION

A firefighter should:

- think quickly, yet act calmly in crisis
- be physically strong and agile
- have some knowledge about machines, electronics, plumbing, construction techniques, chemicals, and automobiles
- be able to get along well with others because firefighters live at the firehouse for 24-hour periods
- be able to compute quickly using formulas

Minimum Education: High-school graduate. Most communities require that applicants pass an examination to qualify for training.

Starting Salary: $20,000–$26,000 per year

Related Careers: Bodyguard, Store Detective

PAINTER

José Fernandez runs a commercial painting business. He and his employees paint all kinds of buildings—hospitals, factories, offices, and warehouses. Commercial painting is a competitive business. Often, several painting companies are interested in taking on the same job. Only one of them will get it. A solid knowledge of mathematics is essential to deciding what price to charge for a job. Any errors in computation that you make could take you out of the competition.

```
            PRECISION TOOL AND DYE COMPANY
        4893 Sheet Metal Rd.  Atlasville, MI  17843


Mr. José Fernandez
M & J Painting Company
389 Clearview Ave.
Atlasville, MI  17843

Dear Mr. Fernandez:

The inside of our factory needs a fresh coat of paint. I'd like you to bid on
this job. Here is some basic information to keep in mind.

   •  You have four days to paint the entire factory.
   •  The factory consists of a shop area, a general office, and my office. The
      bathrooms do not need to be painted.
   •  The building measures 80 ft by 40 ft.
   •  The entire east wall is covered with glass.

Please call my office for an appointment to visit our factory. In the meantime,
here is a blueprint that shows the layout of the factory.

Sincerely,

Greg DeAngelis
President
```

Symbol for Door: (

Door Heights:
- All are 7 ft high, except for the Overhead Door in the shop, which is 12 ft high.

Ceiling Heights:
- Shop — 14 ft
- Offices, hallways, and bathrooms — 8 ft

CALCULATING SQUARE FOOTAGE

José figures out the square footage (area to be painted) of each room and the total square footage of the factory. Use the following equation to calculate the amount of square footage in each room to be painted.

$$\text{Area of Wall} = \text{Length} \times \text{Height}$$
$$A = l \times h$$

ROOM SCHEDULE: PRECISION TOOL AND DYE CO.

	ROOM: SHOP				ROOM: GENERAL OFFICE		
	Wall length	Wall height	Area		Wall length	Wall height	Area
East:	36 ft ×	14 ft	504 sq. ft				

ROOM: SHOP

East: 36 ft × 14 ft = 504 sq. ft

1. West: __28__ ft × __14__ ft __392__ sq. ft

2. South: __50__ ft × __14__ ft __700__ sq. ft

3. North: __50__ ft × __14__ ft __700__ sq. ft

4. TOTAL AREA TO BE PAINTED __1,792__ sq. ft

ROOM: GENERAL OFFICE

5. South: __14__ ft × __8__ ft __112__ sq. ft

6. West: __20__ ft × __8__ ft __160__ sq. ft

7. North: __30__ ft × __8__ ft __240__ sq. ft

8. East: All glass—no painting required

9. TOTAL AREA TO BE PAINTED __512__ sq. ft

96

PAINTER

ROOM: PRESIDENT'S OFFICE	TOTAL SQUARE FOOTAGE

	Wall length	Wall height	Area		Room	Square Footage
10. South:	16 ft ×	8 ft	128 sq. ft	**15.**	Shop	1,792 sq. ft
11. West:	16 ft ×	8 ft	128 sq. ft	**16.**	General Office	512 sq. ft
12. North:	16 ft ×	8 ft	128 sq. ft	**17.**	President's Office	384 sq. ft
13. East: All glass—no painting required				**18.**	Hallways	417 sq. ft

14. TOTAL AREA
TO BE PAINTED ____384____ sq. ft

19. TOTAL AREA
TO BE PAINTED ____2,688____ sq. ft

COMPUTING THE COST OF THE PAINT

A gallon of paint will cover about 250 square feet. Two coats are needed. Calculate the total number of gallons needed to paint the tool-and-dye shop as follows: (Round up the number of gallons to the nearest whole number.)

20. ____2,688____ ÷ ____250____ ≈ ____11____   **21.** ____11____ × ____2____ = ____22____
Total number   Sq. ft per gal   No. of gal. for   Number of gallons   Number   Total number of
of sq. ft   one coat (Round   for one coat   of coats   gallons needed
                                            up)

22. Paint is bought in 5-gallon drums.
How many drums should José buy to paint the entire factory?   **5 drums**

23. The price of a 5-gallon drum of paint is about $100.00.
How much will the paint for this job cost?   **$500**

24. Find 5% of the cost above for ordering and picking up materials.   **$25**

25. TOTAL COST OF MATERIALS   **$525**

CALCULATING LABOR COSTS

José knows from experience that he will need 4 painters to finish the job in 4 days.
Calculate the labor costs.

26.   7   × ____4____ = ____28____
No. of hours   No. of days   Total no. of
in 1 working day   to complete the job   hours per painter

27. ____28____ × ____$25____ = $____700____
Total no. of   Hourly rate   Total cost for
hours per painter   per painter   1 painter

28. ____$700____ × ____4____ = $____2,800____
Total cost of   Number of   LABOR COSTS
1 painter   painters

Don't forget about the doors. Most doors require two coats of paint. Painters usually find it easier just to set a fixed price to paint a door. The price is based on the size of the door.

	Size of door	Price per door	Number of doors	Total Price
29.	2×7	$30	2	$60
30.	3×7	$40	3	$120
31.	4×7	$50	1	$50
32.	12×12	$100	1	$100

33. TOTAL LABOR FOR DOORS $330

Use the data throughout this lesson to complete the worksheet below.

M & J PAINTING COMPANY

34. Proposal for: **Precision Tool and Dye Company**

(Name of Company)

35.	Square footage to be painted:	2,688 sq. ft.
36.	Total cost of materials (from Exercise 25)	$525
37.	Labor, except for doors (from Exercise 28)	$2,800
38.	Labor for doors (from Exercise 33)	$330
39.	Cost of labor and materials	$3,655
40.	Overhead: 50%*	$1,827.50
41.	TOTAL	$5,482.50

*Overhead includes a supervisor, office, travel expenses, and profit. To calculate the amount of overhead, find 50% of the cost of labor and materials. To get the TOTAL, add the overhead to the cost of labor and materials.

INSIDE INFORMATION

A painter should:

- take pride in his workmanship
- work carefully, paying close attention to details
- have a steady hand
- be honest and trustworthy since people allow a painter to work in their offices and homes
- be able to express himself clearly when speaking and writing

Minimum Education: High-school graduate and apprenticeship instruction

Starting Salary: $250–$300 per week as an apprentice painter

Related Careers: Paperhanger, Metal Sprayer

POLICE OFFICER

Susan Matthews is a police officer. If you think the only mathematics a police officer uses is to count the number of arrests made in one week, you're in for a surprise. 24-hour time and Triangulating an Accident are two of the important ways in which Evelyn uses mathematics on the job.

CONVERTING 12-HOUR TIME TO 24-HOUR TIME

Police officers, air traffic controllers, and the military use 24-hour time. In 24-hour time, four digits are used to write the time. The first two digits stand for the hour, the last two stand for the minutes. The day begins at midnight, or 0000 hours. Each hour is written as the number of hours it is past midnight. For example, 9 A.M. is written as 0900 hours; 3:26 P.M. is written as 1526 hours. Because there is no A.M. or P.M., there is never any confusion about whether an event took place during A.M. or P.M. hours.

EQUIVALENT TIMES			
12-hour time	24-hour time	12-hour time	24-hour time
12:00 A.M. (midnight)	0000 hours	12:00 P.M.	1200 hours
1:00 A.M.	0100 hours	1:00 P.M.	1300 hours
2:00 A.M.	0200 hours	2:00 P.M.	1400 hours
3:00 A.M.	0300 hours	3:00 P.M.	1500 hours
4:00 A.M.	0400 hours	4:00 P.M.	1600 hours
5:00 A.M.	0500 hours	5:00 P.M.	1700 hours
6:00 A.M.	0600 hours	6:00 P.M.	1800 hours
7:00 A.M.	0700 hours	7:00 P.M.	1900 hours
8:00 A.M.	0800 hours	8:00 P.M.	2000 hours
9:00 A.M.	0900 hours	9:00 P.M.	2100 hours
10:00 A.M.	1000 hours	10:00 P.M.	2200 hours
11:00 A.M.	1100 hours	11:00 P.M.	2300 hours

Notice that for the morning hours, time is written in very similar ways in 12-hour time and 24-hour time. Study the times from 1:00 P.M. to 11:00 P.M. See if you can discover a pattern between 12-hour time and 24-hour time.

1. To change times between the hours of 1:00 P.M. and 11:59 P.M to the equivalent time on the 24-hour clock, _____**add 12**_____ to the number of hours.

2. To change times between 1300 hours and 2359 hours to the corresponding time on the 12-hour clock, _____**subtract 12**_____ from the number of hours.

Write the following 12-hour times in 24-hour time.

3. 2:00 P.M.   ___**1400 hours**___   4. 5:30 P.M.   ___**1730 hours**___   5. 9:15 P.M.   ___**2115 hours**___

6. 4:45 P.M.   ___**1645 hours**___   7. 11:28 P.M.   ___**2328 hours**___   8. 7:52 P.M.   ___**1952 hours**___

Write the following 24-hour times in 12-hour time. Remember to use A.M. and P.M.

9. 1800 hours _____6:00 P.M._____

10. 2000 hours _____8:00 P.M._____

11. 1330 hours _____1:30 P.M._____

12. 1945 hours _____7:45 P.M._____

13. 2323 hours _____11:23 P.M._____

14. 1705 hours _____5:05 P.M._____

TRIANGULATING AN ACCIDENT

One of a police officer's most important duties is to assist at auto accidents. Police officers help the injured, settle disputes between the people involved in the accident, and issue citations, or tickets, to drivers who have broken the law.

A police officer has to make a diagram of every accident. If one driver sues the other and the case goes to court, the judge usually asks to be shown how the accident happened. The police can reconstruct the accident based on the diagram made at the scene of the accident.

The police officer draws a triangle to show the final position of each car in an accident. This is called *triangulating an accident.* Here are the steps the officer follows to triangulate an accident.

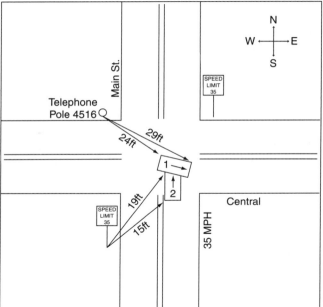

- Choose an object such as a telephone pole or stop sign that is likely to be in the same place many years from now.

- Measure the distance from the telephone pole to the left front tire of one of the cars in the accident.

- Measure the distance from the telephone pole to the left rear tire of the same car.

- Draw a diagram that shows these distances. Include the car, the telephone pole, traffic lights, and any other important landmarks in your drawing. Use an arrow to show which way the car is headed.

- Repeat the steps above for each of the other cars in the accident.

Use the diagram to answer the following questions.

15. What object was used to triangulate the position of Car 1? _____Telephone Pole 4516_____

16. What object was used to triangulate the position of Car 2? _____speed limit sign_____

17. What is the distance from the telephone pole to the left front tire of Car 1? _____29 ft_____

18. What is the distance from the telephone pole to the left rear tire of Car 1? _____24 ft_____

19. Write the distance from the speed-limit sign to the tires in Car 2.

left front tire _____19 ft_____   left rear tire _____15 ft_____

POLICE OFFICER

20. What is the speed limit in the area of the accident shown below? _____ **35 miles per hour**

21. Use the following data and the diagram at the right to triangulate the scene of the accident. Notice that Lake Rd. and Park St. are both one-way streets.

- Car 1 was heading south on Lake Rd. It failed to stop at the stop sign and hit Car 2 as it was going west on Park St.

- Use the stop sign at the northeast corner of Park St. and Lake Rd. as the base for triangulating the position of Car 1.

  — Distance from stop sign to front left tire = 32 ft
  — Distance from stop sign to rear left tire = 27 ft

- Use the lamppost at the southeast corner of Park St. and Lake Rd. as the base for triangulating the position of Car 2.

  — Distance from lamppost to front left tire = 38 ft

  — Distance from lamppost to rear left tire = 26 ft

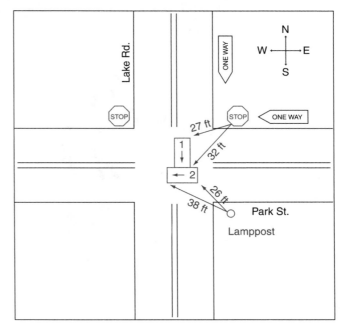

22. Use the following data and the diagram at the right to triangulate the scene of the accident. Notice that Hill St. and Elm St. are two-way streets.

- Car 1 was turning left from Hill St. onto Elm St. It misjudged the speed at which Car 2 was traveling. Car 2 hit the right side of Car 1 as Car 1 was turning left.

- Use the lamppost at the northwest corner of Hill St. and Elm St. as the base for triangulating the position of Car 1.

  — Distance from lamppost to front left tire = 38 ft

  — Distance from lamppost to rear left tire = 45 ft

- Use the street sign at the southeast corner of Hill St. and Elm St. as the base for triangulating the position of Car 2.

  — Distance from street sign to front left tire = 32 ft

  — Distance from street sign to rear tire = 26 ft

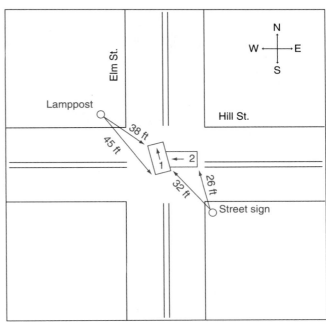

INSIDE INFORMATION

A police officer should:

- always be alert
- be willing to work under dangerous and stressful conditions
- have good vision, hearing, strength, and agility
- be honest
- have a high sense of responsibility and integrity

Minimum Education: Some college education

Starting Salary: $19,200–$25,700 per year

Related Careers: Detective, Correctional Officer

ELECTRICIAN

Seven years ago Jason Champion was a waiter. His customers would usually say, "What's cooking today?" But one day an electrician who was a regular customer looked at Jason and asked, "Would you like a change? Suppose I train you to become an electrician."

Today, Jason is a licensed electrician. He is in the process of installing electrical wire and outlets in an apartment that is being completely remodeled.

There are 4 steps that Jason will take in wiring the apartment:

1. Interpreting the Layout   2. Planning Loads   3. Computing the Costs   4. Making the Installations

INTERPRETING THE LAYOUT

The architect has already given Jason a scale drawing of the apartment he will be wiring. Usually, these architectural plans are drawn to the scale $\frac{1}{4}$ in. = 1 ft. Jason must then figure out the true dimensions of the apartment. Then Jason makes his own drawings. These drawings help him in planning the new wiring. One of his drawings is shown below:

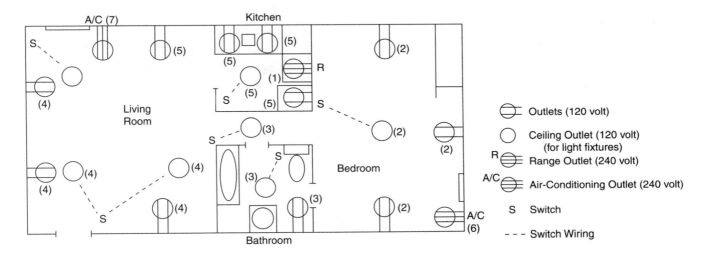

The number in parentheses beside each symbol tells which circuit furnishes power to the outlet. These numbers also appear in the fuse box.

1. Which circuits furnish power to the bedroom?

   _____ 2 (lights and outlets): 6 (A/C) _____

2. Which circuit furnishes power to the range?

   _____ 1 _____

3. If the lights in the kitchen go out, which circuit should you check in the fuse box? __ 5 _____

4. How many ceiling outlets are planned for the living room? __3__

5. What is the total number of 120-volt wall and ceiling outlets in the apartment? __18__

PLANNING LOADS

Every city or town has electrical codes, or guidelines, that electricians have to follow when wiring a house. The codes help prevent electrical fires. Jason uses the following formula to help him calculate the load of electricity a circuit can take:

Amps × Volts = Watts (Load of electricity)

6. Residential (home) lighting uses 15-amp circuits. Most homes have outlets that carry 120 volts of electricity.

What is the greatest number of watts a circuit for home lighting can take?

__1,800 watts__

Lightbulbs come in different wattages. Complete the chart below to find out how many light fixtures Jason can put on 1 circuit for each type of bulb.

Maximum Number of Watts	÷	Number of Watts	=	Number of Fixtures
7. 1,800	÷	60	=	30
8. 1,800	÷	75	=	24
9. 1,800	÷	100	=	18
10. 1,800	÷	150	=	12

11. Suppose Jason plans to use bulbs of different watts in the fixtures. Will eight 100-watt bulbs and eleven 75-watt bulbs overload the circuit? What is the total wattage?

__No. Total wattage is 1,625 watts.__

12. What is the total wattage for six 150-watt bulbs and twelve 60-watt bulbs? __1,620 watts__

Circuits for appliances carry a greater load of electricity (more watts).

- Appliance circuits can be 20 amps.
- The circuit can handle 120 volts.
- The electrical code requires 2 appliance circuits in each kitchen.

Remember: Amps × Volts = Watts

13. What is the greatest number of watts an appliance circuit can carry? __2,400 watts__

14. Can a 1,350-watt microwave and a 1,500-watt refrigerator run on the same appliance circuit? Explain your answer.

__No. Their total wattage is 2,850 watts.__

Name _____ Class _____ Date _____

ELECTRICIAN

15. There is a 1,500-watt dishwasher and a 1,500-watt refrigerator in the kitchen. Does their total wattage go over the maximum load an appliance circuit can carry? If so, by how much? How would you handle this problem as an electrician?

Yes, by 600 watts. The problem could be solved by installing another circuit.

16. Electric stoves and electric dryers require 240-watt outlets. What is the maximum load an appliance circuit can carry to a 240-volt outlet if it's 20 amps? __**4,800 watts**__

When planning the load of electricity, Jason has to consider other requirements of the electrical code.

- There should be an electrical outlet every 15 feet along the walls.
- There should be an A/C (air-conditioning) outlet in every room except the kitchen and bathroom.

Follow the steps below to plan the loads for the following apartment.

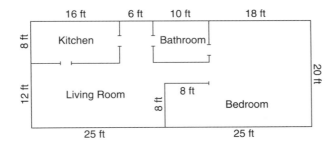

Step A: Complete the following chart to determine the number of outlets for each room.
Round <u>up</u> to the nearest whole number. The first one is done for you.

Room	Wall Lengths	Perimeter	÷	15 ft	=	Quotient	Number of Outlets Needed
Living Room	25, 12, 16, 8	61	÷	15	=	4.06	5
17. Bedroom	18, 20, 25, 8, 8, 8	87	÷	15	=	5.8	6
18. Kitchen	8, 16, 8, 16	48	÷	15	=	3.2	4
19. Bathroom	8, 10, 8, 10	36	÷	15	=	2.4	3

20. Total Number of Outlets in Apartment: __18__

Step B: Look at Jason's drawing on page 103. Use those symbols to show where you would position the 120-volt outlets, ceiling outlets, and switches on the diagram above.

Check students' diagrams.

21. In questions 17–19, you calculated how many outlets each room must have. Then you decided where to place the outlets. What factors did you consider when positioning outlets in the living room?

Answers will vary, but may include convenience, placement of furniture, and length of

walls.

USING FORMULAS, MEASUREMENT, AND GEOMETRY

105

Complete the calculations on the following bill.

JASON CHAMPION	ELECTRICIAN
To: Aaron Cartwright 19 Berkeley Place Brooklyn, NY 11208	Date: February 9, 1999

MATERIALS AND INSTALLATION

- 2 two-wire @ $55.00/coil $ 110.00
- 1 three-wire @ $75.00/coil   **22.** $ 75.00
- 3 "dedicated" lines @ $130.00/line   **23.** $ 390.00
- 12 boxes (outlets) @ $65.00/box   **24.** $ 780.00
- 15 light outlets @ $40.00/light   **25.** $ 600.00

Total: Materials and Installation   **26.** $ 1,955.00

---

*I*NSIDE *I*NFORMATION

An electrician should:

- like to work with machines and gadgets
- be able to determine the causes of problems
- know how buildings are constructed
- be able to locate and trace wiring behind walls
- know the rules of safety

Minimum Education: High-school graduate; apprenticeship of 4–5 years with licensed electrician

Starting Salary: $8,800–$17,000 per year
(or)
$169–$327 per week

Related Careers: Cable Installer, Air-Conditioning Mechanic

CARPENTER

Andy Jackson, a carpenter in Bismarck, North Dakota, lives in a building that he designed. The floor plan of the first floor of his house is shown below. How many square feet of space are there?

USING A FORMULA TO FIND AREA

To find the number of square feet, you need to find the total area of the house. Notice that each room is in the shape of a rectangle. Use the formula $A = l \times w$ to find the area of each room. Remember to give each answer in square feet (sq. ft).

1. What is the area of the bedroom?

   288 sq. ft

2. What is the area of the bathroom?

   60 sq. ft

3. What is the area of the living room and kitchen? **512 sq. ft**

4. What is the total area of the first floor? **860 sq. ft**

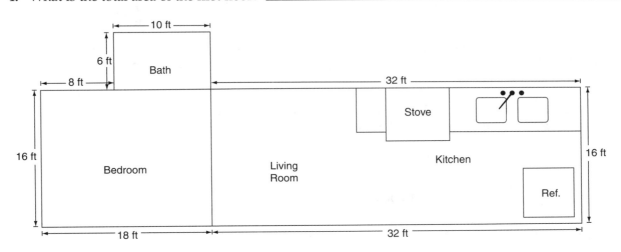

If you want to be a carpenter, you have to be able to measure distances quickly and accurately. This skill is the most basic part of a carpenter's work. Carpenters have to measure actual objects such as walls, cabinets, and tables. They also have to be able to measure lines on diagrams.

Use a ruler. Measure each of the following line segments to the nearest inch, nearest $\frac{1}{2}$ inch, nearest $\frac{1}{4}$ inch, and nearest $\frac{1}{8}$ inch.

5. nearest inch **3 in.**

6. nearest $\frac{1}{2}$ inch **$3\frac{1}{2}$ in.**

7. nearest $\frac{1}{4}$ inch **$3\frac{1}{4}$ in.**

8. nearest $\frac{1}{8}$ in. **$3\frac{3}{8}$ in.**

9. nearest inch   _____6 in._____   10. nearest $\frac{1}{2}$ inch   _____$5\frac{1}{2}$ in._____

11. nearest $\frac{1}{4}$ inch   _____$5\frac{3}{4}$ in._____   12. nearest $\frac{1}{8}$ inch   _____$5\frac{6}{8}$ or $5\frac{3}{4}$ in._____

A carpenter also has to know how to use a ruler when drawing models of homes, cabinets, bookcases, and so on.

Draw a line segment for each of the following lengths.

13. 4 in.

14. $5\frac{1}{2}$ in.

15. $1\frac{1}{4}$ in.   **Check students' drawings.**

16. $2\frac{7}{8}$ in.

Andy is building a kitchen counter. He cuts each piece of wood $\frac{1}{4}$ in. longer than the plan calls for.

(If a piece of wood is too long, you can cut it shorter. But if it is too short, you can't make it longer.) Following this rule, how long should Andy cut each of the following pieces of the drawer?

17. 15 in.   _____$15\frac{1}{4}$ in._____   18. $6\frac{3}{4}$ in.   _____7 in._____

19. $20\frac{1}{4}$ in.   _____$20\frac{1}{2}$ in._____   20. $8\frac{5}{8}$ in.   _____$8\frac{7}{8}$ in._____

21. $7\frac{1}{2}$ in.   _____$7\frac{3}{4}$ in._____   22. $4\frac{3}{16}$ in.   _____$4\frac{7}{16}$ in._____

The day after Andy finishes building and installing the kitchen counter, his telephone rings. A man who owns a photo lab is calling. "I want the finest sales counter in the state!" the man says. "How much will that cost me?"

"You can expect to pay about $600 per foot for the very finest counter. A really nice counter will cost you about $350 per foot," Andy answers. "That's assuming the counter is 30 inches wide."

The owner says, "I want a counter about 25 feet long."

23. What would the total cost be for the very best counter at $600 per foot? _____**$15,000**_____

"I've got $10,000 to spend," the owner says.

Andy makes the following calculation:

Budget ÷ Number of Feet = Cost Per Foot
$10,000 ÷   25 ft   = $400 per foot

"I think we're in business," he tells the owner.

CARPENTER

COMPLETING A BID AND PAY SCHEDULE

Andy makes a list of materials he will need to build the photo lab counter. He includes the prices of the materials.

Complete the list.

MATERIAL	AMOUNT	UNIT PRICE	TOTAL
24. $\frac{3}{4}$ in. oak	16 sheets	$52.25/sheet	$ __836.00__
25. $\frac{3}{4}$ in. melamine	4 sheets	$26.65/sheet	$ __106.60__
26. White oak $1\frac{1}{2}$ in. thick	28 board feet	$ __4.50__ /bd ft	$ 126.00
27. Contact cement	2 gallons	$28.99/gallon	$ __57.98__

An estimate of the total cost of building the counter will be given to the photo lab owner.

Complete the bid.

Materials	$ 1,126.58
28. Labor: 205 hours × $20.00/hour	$ __4,100.00__
29. Factor for lost time: 15% of Materials and Labor	+ __783.99__
30. Subtotal	$ __6,010.57__
31. Tax: 8% of Subtotal	+ __480.85__
32. Total Estimate:	$ __6,491.42__

33. Is the estimate more than or less than the owner's $10,000 budget? __less than__

A pay schedule is drawn up. Pick up the total cost from the above estimate and complete the pay schedule.

To: Speedy-Quick Photo Lab	
34. Total Cost:	$ __6,491.42__
35. $\frac{1}{3}$ down	$ __2,163.81__
36. $\frac{1}{3}$ at midpoint	$ __2,163.81__
37. $\frac{1}{3}$ on completion	$ __2,163.80__

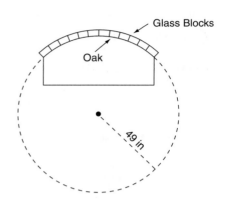

For some counters that Andy builds, the front of the counter is a curve. This curve is $\frac{1}{4}$ of a circle. The manufacturer provides the radius for the circle. A thin piece of oak covers the curve. The oak is cut in a straight piece and bent to fit the curve. Then glass blocks cover the oak as a final touch.

The curve is $\frac{1}{4}$ of a circle with a radius of 49 in. Andy follows these steps to determine the length of the piece of oak.

Step 1: Find the circumference. Use the formula $C = 2\pi r$. Recall that C is the circumference and r is the radius.

$$C = 2\pi r$$
$$C \approx 2 \times \frac{22}{7} \times 49 \text{ in.}$$
$$C \approx 2 \times 154 \text{ in.}$$
$$C \approx 308 \text{ in.}$$

Step 2: The length of the curve is $\frac{1}{4}$ of the circumference. Divide the circumference by 4.

$$308 \text{ in.} \div 4 = 77$$

$\approx$ means *approximately equal to*

Andy should cut a strip of oak that measures 77 in.

Follow the steps above to complete the following table.

	Radius of Circle	Length of Oak to Be Cut
38.	42 in.	66 in.
39.	21 in.	33 in.
40.	56 in.	88 in.

INSIDE INFORMATION

A carpenter should:

- be able to visualize how objects will look when built
- have a solid knowledge of such mathematical topics as measurement, perimeter, area, and volume
- be able to meet deadlines
- work carefully and pay attention to details
- know rules of safety when operating machinery

Minimum Education: High-school graduate   *Starting Salary:* $9–$15 per hour

Related Careers: Bricklayer, Pipefitter

*L*ANDSCAPER

Gail Brown works as a landscaper in Baton Rouge, Louisiana. Her company specializes in landscaping and maintaining business properties. A small shopping center has asked Gail to give them an estimate for landscaping and maintaining its grounds.

A work crew measures the various sections of the grounds. Gail draws a diagram of one flower bed. She wants to find the area of this T-shaped bed. To double-check her calculations, Gail asks the crew supervisor to find the area also.

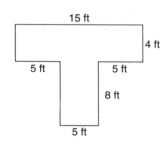

Both of them: • divide the bed into rectangles;

• find the area of each rectangle;

• add the areas together to find the total area.

They divide the bed into rectangles in different ways.

GAIL

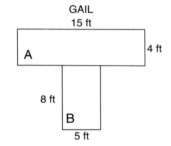

CREW SUPERVISOR

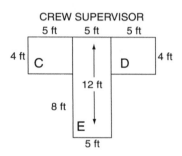

Find the areas of the rectangles in each diagram. Then find the total area. Use the formula:

$$Area = length \times width$$
$$A = lw$$

GAIL:

Area of A: _____ 15 × 4 = 60 sq. ft _____

1. Area of B: _____ 8 × 5 = 40 sq. ft _____

2. Area of bed: _____ 100 sq. ft _____

CREW SUPERVISOR:

3. Area of C: _____ 5 × 4 = 20 sq. ft _____

4. Area of D: _____ 5 × 4 = 20 sq. ft _____

5. Area of E: _____ 12 × 5 = 60 sq. ft _____

6. Area of bed: _____ 100 sq. ft _____

7. Are the answers the same? _____ Yes _____

Gail decides to plant a shrub called dwarf jasmine along the border of the T-shaped flower bed. This small shrub grows 1 foot high and 2 feet across. Use the diagram to the right to estimate the number of shrubs Gail should order.

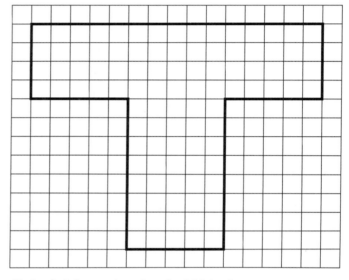

Notice that the distance between lines stands for 1 foot. Remember to leave at least 1 foot of space between shrubs.

8. About how many shrubs should Gail order?

   Answers will vary.

Gail takes her notes and sketches back to the office. If she finishes estimating the bid in the afternoon, it can be shown to the owners of the shopping center tomorrow. Unfortunately, there are many interruptions. Within a space of fifteen minutes, the following things happen:

a. A truckload of white rosebushes is delivered. Gail had ordered yellow rosebushes.

b. A customer has heard that a freeze is due overnight. He calls to insist that a crew be sent over to cover the palm trees in front of his building. All of the crews are out on jobs already.

c. A crew supervisor calls in to report a riding mower has broken down.

d. A member of a work crew is having trouble with her supervisor and wants to be transferred to another crew.

e. A fertilizer salesperson is on the telephone to take Gail's monthly order.

9. In which order would you handle the problems?

   Answers will vary.

10. What would you do in each situation?

   Answers will vary.

Name _____ Class _____ Date _____

LANDSCAPER

Gail's next task is to plan a flower garden for a bank. The president of the bank has decided on purple and yellow petunias. Here are Gail's notes on the job.

- The flower bed measures 31 feet by 7 feet.
- Petunias should be spaced 1 foot apart.
- There should be a 1-foot border between the flowers and the edge of the flower bed.
- $\frac{1}{3}$ of the petunias should be yellow, $\frac{2}{3}$ should be purple.

This grid shows the flower bed. The distance between lines stands for 1 foot.

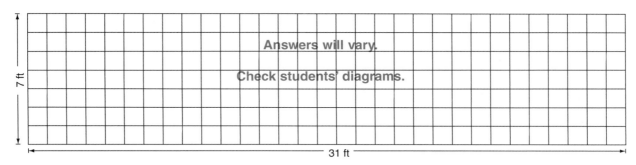

11. What is the area of the flower bed? _____ 217 sq. ft _____

12. How many petunias will fit within the flower bed? _____ 180 petunias _____

13. How many petunias will be yellow? _____ 60 petunias will be yellow _____

14. How many petunias will be purple? _____ 120 petunias will be purple _____

15. Use the grid above to show a possible arrangement of the petunias in the flower box. Use a small circle for yellow petunias and a small square for purple petunias. (The petunias are to be planted where the lines cross.)

Before Gail left work at 4:30 P.M., she was able to finish the bid for maintaining the grounds at the shopping center.

Complete the forms. Write the fractions as decimals. Round to the nearest cent when necessary.

LANDSCAPE MAINTENANCE BID SHEET

	ACTIVITIES	HOURS PER WEEK	
	Walk Behind (self-propelled mower)	$\frac{3}{4}$ hour	0.75
16.	Push Mow	$1\frac{1}{4}$ hours	1.25
17.	Line Trim/Blowing	$5\frac{1}{2}$ hours	5.50
18.	Tree Work	$\frac{3}{4}$ hour	0.75
19.	Shrub Work	$1\frac{1}{2}$ hours	1.50
20.	Bed Work	3 hours	3.00
21.	Trash	$1\frac{1}{2}$ hours	1.50
22.	Travel to/from site	1 hour	1.00
23.	TOTAL		15.25 hours

Gail then uses 15.25 hours of labor per week as an estimate for the fall, spring, and summer. She estimates 8 hours per week for the winter.

ANNUAL LABOR COSTS

	Average Hourly Wage	×	Hours Per Week	×	Number of Months in Season	×	Number of Weeks Per Month	=	Total Labor
24.	$10.25	×	15.25	×	9 (fall, spring, summer)	×	4.33	= $	6,091.50
25.	$10.25	×	8.00	×	3 (winter)	×	4.33	= $	1,065.18
26.	TOTAL							= $	7,156.68

TOTAL MONTHLY COSTS:

	Total Labor for Year	×	(Factor for Taxes, Materials, Overhead, Profit)*	=	Total Annual Cost
27.	$7,156.68	×	2	= $	14,313.36

	Total Annual Cost	÷	12 months	=	Total Monthly Cost
28.	$14,313.36	÷	12	= $	1,192.78 (to the nearest cent)

*Overhead means office expenses such as rent, telephone, electricity, supplies.
Multiplying by 2 allows for taxes, materials, overhead, and profit.

INSIDE INFORMATION

A landscaper should:

- know about plants and their care
- enjoy working outdoors
- be able to coordinate various activities at the same time
- have a solid understanding of perimeter and area
- be able to compute with whole numbers and decimals

Minimum Education: High-school graduate   *Starting Salary:* $180–$220 per week

Related Careers: Botanist, Forest Conservation Worker

AIR TRAFFIC CONTROLLER

Dennis Sauer is an air traffic controller with the Federal Aviation Agency (FAA) in Austin, Texas. In 1986 he received his pilot's license and flew professionally before becoming a controller. Today, Dennis works in the Air Route Traffic Control Center.

- An airplane that is 40 to 100 miles away from Austin is handled by a regional controller in either San Antonio (south), Gray Air Force Base (north), or Houston (east and west).

- The Center in Austin is responsible for all aircraft flying higher than 3,000 feet and 5 to 40 miles from the airport.

- The Center also handles "fly-throughs," airplanes that are flying lower than 11,000 feet but are not landing at the Austin airport.

- As an airplane flying into Austin reaches the 5-mile limit or descends to an altitude of 3,000 feet or less, the pilot is handed off to the Austin airport control tower.

- All airplanes on the ground traveling to and from runways are handled by the control tower.

USING DISTANCE TO DETERMINE THE AIR TRAFFIC CONTROLLER

Write TOWER for the Austin airport control tower, CENTER for the Air Route Traffic Center, or REGIONAL for one of the three regional control centers.

1. An airplane that took off from the Austin airport and is 7 miles away from the airport at an altitude of 11,000 feet   **CENTER**

2. An airplane flying from Johnson City to Houston over Austin at an altitude of 10,000 feet.   **CENTER**

3. An airplane at an altitude of 2,500 feet preparing to land at the Austin airport.   **TOWER**

4. An airplane 42 miles south of the Austin airport.   **REGIONAL**

5. An airplane at an altitude of 5,000 feet beginning its final approach to the Austin airport 37 miles away.   **CENTER**

6. An airplane at 4,800 feet after taking off from the Austin airport.   **CENTER**

7. An airplane 96 miles east of the Austin airport.   **REGIONAL**

8. An airplane that has just left Gate 24 on its way to runway 29 at the Austin airport.   **TOWER**

DETERMINING AIR SPEED AND DISTANCE

Air traffic controllers must have an idea of how fast airplanes fly. For instance, if an airplane flying in from the east is 40 miles away, they must be able to estimate when it will get to the airport.

Use the table below to answer the following questions.

TYPE OF AIRCRAFT	APPROXIMATE SPEED ON FINAL APPROACH
F4 fighter plane	450 miles per hour
Small private plane	2 miles per minute
Commercial airliner	4 miles per minute

9. If a small private plane is 40 miles east of the Austin airport and a commercial airliner is 40 miles west of it, which plane will reach the airport first?

    commercial airliner

10. About how many minutes will it take the commercial airliner to reach the airport?

    about 10 minutes

11. About how many minutes will it take the small private plane to reach the airport?

    about 20 minutes

12. How many miles per minute can an F4 fly?

    7.5 miles per minute

13. A private plane is about 8 minutes away from landing at the Austin airport. About how far is the plane from the airport?

    16 miles

14. An F4 is 30 miles from the Austin airport. A small private plane is 3 minutes away from the airport. Which plane will arrive first?

    small plane

15. A commercial airliner is 15 minutes away from landing at the Austin airport. In how many minutes will it be handed over to a controller at the Austin Center?

    5 minutes

USING COORDINATED UNIVERSAL TIME (UTC)

The Federal Aviation Agency uses Greenwich Mean Time. This is also known as Coordinated Universal Time (UTC) and is based on the 24-hour clock. In 0905, for example, the first two digits indicate the hour and the last two digits show the minutes. An air traffic controller would say, "Zero Niner Zero Five." In radio transmissions, the number "9" is read as "niner." All the other numbers from 0 to 8 are read normally.

To change UTC to any of the Standard Time Zones in the United States, use the following table.

To change 0905 in UTC to Pacific Standard Time, subtract 8 hours:

0905 UTC = 9 h 5 min – 8 h = 1 h 5 min,
or 0105 PST

To change a time after 1300 hours (1:00 P.M.) on the 24-hour clock to an equivalent time on the 12–hour clock, subtract 1200.

What time is 1845 equivalent to on the 12-hour clock?

1845 – 1200 = 0645 or 6:45 P.M.

TO CHANGE FROM COORDINATED UNIVERSAL TIME (UTC)	
To	Subtract
Eastern Standard Time	5 hours
Central Standard Time	6 hours
Mountain Standard Time	7 hours
Pacific Standard Time	8 hours
Alaska Standard Time	9 hours
Hawaii Standard Time	10 hours

Air Traffic Controller

Calculate the correct time.

16. It is 0905 UTC. What time is it in the Eastern Standard Time zone?

_____ 0405, or 4:05 A.M. _____

17. It is "One Two Two Zero" UTC. Write this time using A.M. or P.M. on the 12-hour clock.

_____ 12:20 P.M. _____

18. A pilot radios the control tower on his final approach to Los Angeles. He says that his Estimated Time of Arrival (ETA) is Zero Five Five Niner. What is the ETA in Los Angeles?

_____ 0559, or 5:59 A.M. _____

19. An airliner is scheduled to depart from Chicago's O'Hare Airport for Rome at 2035 hours. Write this departure time using A.M. or P.M. on the 12-hour clock.

_____ 8:35 P.M. _____

20. The time in Denver is 4:00 A.M., Mountain Standard Time. What time is it in UTC?

_____ 1100 hours _____

21. A flight from Paris arrives in Washington, D.C. at 2:40 P.M. Write this arrival time using the 24-hour clock.

_____ 1440 hours _____

MEASURING DISTANCES BETWEEN PLANES

To ensure safety in the skies, there are rules regarding how close airplanes can be. In most cases, two airplanes must be

- at least 1,000 feet vertically apart (above or below) or
- at least 3 miles apart horizontally (on either side)

22. One commercial airliner is flying at 31,000 feet. Another airliner has leveled off at 29,500 feet. How far apart are they vertically?

_____ 1,500 feet _____

23. A corporate jet has climbed to 43,250 feet. Five miles to the north an F4 is flying parallel at 43,250 feet. Are the planes a safe distance apart?

_____ yes _____

24. A small private plane is flying at 17,860 feet. A corporate jet is flying at 18,086 feet. How far apart are the two planes vertically?

_____ 226 feet _____

25. A commercial airliner is flying at an altitude of 36,010 feet. What are the altitudes above and below that a nearby plane can fly?

_____ 35,010 ft; 37,010 ft _____

USING FLIGHT MAPS AND FLIGHT PLANS

Pilots use flight maps to chart their flight plans.

- An airplane flying below 18,000 feet may fly on visual meteorological conditions (VMC). This means that ground landmarks such as lakes, antennas, ranches, and highways are used to navigate.

- Instrument meteorological conditions (IMC) rely on an airplane's instruments to navigate air routes. A pilot must be certified to fly by instrumentation.

The map on the next page shows high altitude instrument flight routes (IFR). This map is for use at and above 18,000 feet. When a plane takes off, an air traffic controller assigns it to a route with a name such as J17 or J4-42. These sky routes are like the lanes on a highway. Pilots find the correct route and stay on course by following a compass reading called a **heading.** A heading of 070 means that the route that the plane will take is at a 70° angle clockwise from the north.

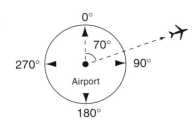

As the plane flies, it is transferred from one air traffic controller to another who changes its course by instructing the pilot to follow a different heading.

AIR ROUTES TO AND FROM ABILENE AIRPORT

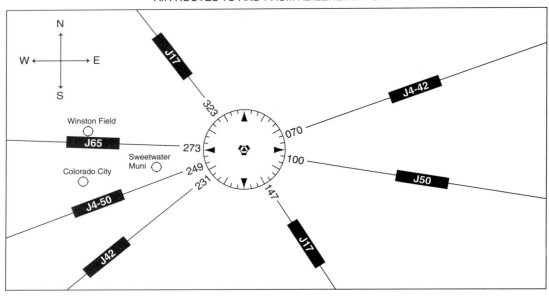

26. What is the heading of an airplane flying *out* of Abilene on air route J4-42? In which direction is it flying?

070, northeast

27. What is the heading of an airplane flying *out* of Abilene on air route J65? In which direction is it flying?

273, west

28. Which air route has a heading of 231?

J42

29. A plane takes off from Abilene heading 231. In which direction is the plane flying?

southwest

INSIDE INFORMATION

An air traffic controller should:

- have good vision
- be able to work under stress
- possess a good speaking voice
- be a good listener
- be a fast thinker
- have the ability to visualize in 3 dimensions what the radar screen shows in 2 dimensions

Minimum Education: High-school graduate; 3 years of work experience or college degree; must pass test and complete 3-month training program

Starting Salaries: $29,500–$31,000

Related Careers: Airline Dispatcher, Air Traffic Coordinator

Quick Math Reference Guide

UNIT 1

New Balance = Previous Balance − (Payments + Credits + Adjustments) + Transactions + Finance Charges

Total Available Credit = Total Credit Line − New Balance

Average Daily Balance = Balance Day 1 + …. Balance Day 31/Total # Days

Total Price of Supplies = Quantity(Unit Price)

Supposed End Cash = Beginning Cash + Business Income − Total Payouts

Cash at End of Shift = Cash at Beginning of Shift + Cash In − Cash Out

Converting Pounds to Cups = (# pounds/5) × # cups per 5 lb. bag

Total Short Term Insurance Premium =
   [(Basic Daily Rate(Policy Period in days) (ZIP Code Factor)] + $15.00 Policy Fee

Converting Weight in Pounds to Kilograms (approx.) = (Weight in lbs. × 1 kg)/2 lbs.

Converting Weight Loss in kg to Fluid Loss in liters = (Weight in kilograms × 1 L)/1 kg

Hourly Rate of Fluid Loss = Fluid Loss in Liters/Total hours

UNIT 2

Solving Proportions
   $a/b = c/d$ $a(d) = b(c)$

Converting a Percentage to a Number = Percentage × .01

Converting a Fraction to a Decimal = Nominator divided by denominator

Converting a Fraction to a Percentage = (Nominator divided by denominator) × 100

Determining a Total Price from a Unit Price = Quantity × Unit Price

Using a Proportion to Determine an Unknown Dimension
   8 inches/10 inches = 4 inches/? inches
                  8(?) = 10 × 4
                     ? = 40/8
                     ? = 5

Calculating the Total Interest Charged on a Car Loan
   Total amount to be paid back − Amount borrowed = Total Interest Charged

UNIT 3

Friction Loss per 100 feet = 2Q(Q) + Q
   Q = # gallons per minute (gpm)/100

Engine Pressure (EP) = Nozzle Pressure (NP) + Total Friction Loss (TFL)

Area of a Wall = Length × Height
   $A = l \times h$

Perimeter of a Building = length of all walls

Area of a Rectangle = length × width
   $A = lw$

Circumference of a Circle = 2(3.14)radius

FEATURED CAREERS

Bulleted items are related careers.

PHOTO CREDITS

Interior:

Unit Opener 1: Secretary, p. 1, Michael Newman/PhotoEdit

Banker (Personal Banker), p. 3, Dana White/PhotoEdit

Secretary, p. 10, Michael Newman/PhotoEdit

Restaurant Manager, p. 12, Amy C. Etra/PhotoEdit

Cashier, p. 15, Tony Freeman/PhotoEdit

Chef, p. 19, Jeff Greenberg/Visuals Unlimited

Insurance Agent, p. 23, David Young-Wolff/PhotoEdit

Registered Nurse, p. 27, Mark Richards/PhotoEdit

Postal Clerk, p. 34, Mark E. Gibson/PhotoEdit

Plumber, p. 35, Tony Freeman/PhotoEdit

Dental Assistant, p. 39, Martha McBride/Unicorn Stock Photos

Unit Opener 2: Auto Mechanic, p. 43, Pat Olear/PhotoEdit

Interior Designer, p. 45, Jeff Greenberg/Unicorn Stock Photos

Photographer, p. 49, Mark E. Gibson/Visuals Unlimited

Home Health Aide, p. 53, Tony Freeman/PhotoEdit

Customer Service Representative, p. 57, Chuck Schmeiser/Unicorn Stock Photos

Travel Agent, p. 63, Michael Newmann/PhotoEdit

Home Economist, p. 65, Bill Bachmann/PhotoEdit

Auto Mechanic, p. 69, Pat Olear/PhotoEdit

Department Store Clerk, p. 73, Jeff Greenberg/PhotoEdit

Graphic Designer, p. 77, Michael Newmann/PhotoEdit

Automobile Salesperson, p. 83, Bill Bachmann/PhotoEdit

Unit Opener 3: Carpenter, p. 85, Jeff Greenberg/Visuals Unlimited

Computer Programmer, p. 87, David Young-Wolff/PhotoEdit

Firefighter, p. 91, Mark Richards/PhotoEdit

Painter, p. 96, Myrleen Ferguson/PhotoEdit

Police Officer, p. 102, Eric Berndt/Unicorn Stock Photos

Electrician, p. 104, D & I MacDonald/Unicorn Stock Photos

Carpenter, p. 107, Jeff Greenberg/Visuals Unlimited

Landscaper, p. 112, Rachel Epstein/PhotoEdit

Air Traffic Controller, p. 115, Mark E. Gibson/Visuals Unlimited

INDEX